TE

en

When I Was Five I Killed Myself

Herausgegeben von
Ernst Kemmner

Philipp Reclam jun. Stuttgart

Diese Ausgabe darf nur in der Bundesrepublik Deutschland, in Österreich und in der Schweiz vertrieben werden.

RECLAMS UNIVERSAL-BIBLIOTHEK Nr. 9100
Alle Rechte vorbehalten
Copyright für diese Ausgabe
© 2002 Philipp Reclam jun. GmbH & Co., Stuttgart
Copyright für den Text © 1981, 2000 Howard Buten.
Abdruck mit Genehmigung von The Overlook Press, New York
Gesamtherstellung: Reclam, Ditzingen
Erstmalig erschienen in den USA unter dem Titel
When I Was Five I Killed Myself
Printed in Germany 2009
RECLAM, UNIVERSAL-BIBLIOTHEK und RECLAMS
UNIVERSAL-BIBLIOTHEK sind eingetragene Marken
der Philipp Reclam jun. GmbH & Co., Stuttgart
ISBN 978-3-15-009100-5

www.reclam.de

Preface

I wrote my first novel when I was eleven. It was a war
epic about the German resistance during the rise of the
Third Reich, a saga of two friends torn apart by the
horrors of war and conflicting ideologies. It was sweeping. It was heartbreaking. It was *The Mortal Storm*, a
Jimmy Stewart movie I'd seen the night before on
television. (A scandal! No one would publish my novel!
What did they mean, it had to be typed?)

I'm an ingrate. It's a personality trait I have. Ever
since I was a child I've thought that the world owes me
a living.

The book you hold in your hand was originally published in 1981 by a major American publishing house
under the title *Burt*. As a tribute to my genius the publisher decided to use it as the object of an innovative

---

3 **epic:** Epos.
4 **Third Reich:** Ära Adolf Hitlers und der NSDAP in Deutschland
  (1933–45).
  saga: Saga; hier: Lebensgeschichte.
  to tear s.o. apart: jdn. auseinander reißen, trennen.
5f. **sweeping** (coll.): radikal, einschneidend; ergreifend.
6 **"The Mortal Storm":** Titel eines Films von 1940.
7 **Stewart:** James St. (1908–97), berühmter amerikanischer Filmschau-
  spieler.
10 **ingrate:** undankbarer und unbequemer Mensch.
  trait: (Charakter-)Zug.
15 **tribute:** Tribut, Zeichen der Anerkennung.
16 **innovative:** innovativ, neuartig.

marketing experiment. It was sweeping. It was heart-breaking. If the world owed me a living, I was obviously going to have to settle out of court. And out of town … way out. *Burt* wound up being published in France, in French, under its present title. It became a cult bestseller, a sort of French *Catcher in the Rye*. (If you believe statistics, *When I Was Five …* has been read by one out of every ten French people who know how to read.) The translation by Jean-Pierre Carasso is a work of genius; my five other novels have enjoyed success; I've even been made a *Chevalier* in the *Ordre des Arts et des Lettres*.

But I'm an ingrate. It's a personality trait I have. *When I Was Five I Killed Myself* is an American novel that I wrote in English to be read in English.

One day a man named Nicolas Hansen, a German publisher, was talking to Peter Mayer, an American publisher. Peter remembered having read the book back in the days of the marketing experiment. It is thanks to him that you are holding it in your hand.

Like everybody else who's been writing novels since they were eleven, there are things in print that I'd write differently now. The republication of *When I Was*

---

3 **to settle out of court:** sich außergerichtlich einigen; Wortspiel mit *to settle* ›sich niederlassen‹.
4 **way out** (coll.): weit weg.
  to wind up: landen, enden.
6 **"The Catcher in the Rye":** Roman (1951) des amerikanischen Schriftstellers J. D. Salinger.
11 **Chevalier** (Fr.): Ritter.
11 f. **Ordre des Arts et des Lettres** (Fr.): Orden der Künste und Literatur.
23 **republication:** Wiederveröffentlichung, Neuauflage.

Five I Killed Myself (written over four years when I was in my early thirties) gives me the chance to do this. But I've been prudent in the fixing. There has always been something in the novel that floats above the page, something that I never put there on purpose. I still don't know how it got there, but I know it when I see it. I kept my hands off.

Books are like babies. They come out from inside you, and once out you want people to hold them in their hands. They don't have to love them, just hold them in their hands. People holding my books makes me happy. It's a personality trait I have.

HOWARD BUTEN
Paris, January 2000

---

3 **prudent:** umsichtig, wohl überlegt.
  fixing: Überarbeitung.
4 **to float above the page:** etwa: zwischen den Zeilen liegen.
7 **to keep one's hands off:** (von etwas) die Finger lassen, nicht (an etwas) rühren.

1

When I was five I killed myself.

I was waiting for Popeye who comes after the News. He has large wrists for a person and he is strong to the finish. But the News wouldn't end.

My dad was watching it. I had my hands over my ears because I am afraid of the News. I don't enjoy it as television. It has Russians on who will bury us. It has the President of the United States who is bald. It has highlights from this year's fabulous Autorama where I have been once, it was quite enjoyable as an activity.

A man came on the News. He had something in his hand, a doll, and he held it up. (You could see it wasn't real because of the sewing.) I took my hands off.

"This was a little girl's favorite toy," the man said. "And tonight, because of a senseless accident, she is dead."

I ran up to my room.

I jumped on my bed.

I stuffed my face into my pillow and pushed it harder and harder until I couldn't hear anything anymore. I held my breath.

---

3 **Popeye:** Comic-Figur; Seemann, der durch Spinatkost zu übernatürlichen Kräften kommt.

4f. **to the finish** (coll.): bis zum Umfallen, wahnsinnig, überaus.

8 **to bury** (coll.): hier: fertig machen.

10 **Autorama:** Automobilausstellung.

15 **sewing:** Naht.

Then my dad came in and took my pillow away and put his hand on me and said my name. I was crying. He bent over and put his hands under me and lifted me up. He did this to the back of my hair and I put my head on him. He is very strong.

He whispered, "It's ok, Son, don't cry."

"I'm not," I said "I'm a big boy."

But I was crying. Then Dad told me that every day somebody gets dead and nobody knows why. It's just the rules. Then he went downstairs.

I sat on my bed for a long time. I sat and sat. Something was wrong inside me, I felt it inside my stomach and I didn't know what to do. So I layed down on the floor. I stuck out my pointer finger and pointed it at my head. And I pushed down my thumb. And killed myself.

---

9 f. **it's just the rules** (coll.): das ist halt so.
13 **layed:** *lay.*
14 **pointer finger:** Zeigefinger.

2

I am at the Children's Trust Residence Center.

I am here for what I did to Jessica. My nose is still
bleeding but it doesn't hurt, but my face is black and
5 blue on my cheek. It hurts. I am ashamed.

When I got here the first person I met was Mrs
Cochrane. She came to meet me at the desk where I
was with my mom and dad. Everybody shook hands
but me. I had my hands in my pockets. They were fists.
10 Mrs Cochrane took me away. She is ugly. I could ralph
looking at her and she wears slacks even though she is
old. She talks very quiet to me like I am sleeping. I'm
not sleeping.

She took me to my wing. It has six beds in it. No cur-
15 tains, no rugs. No dressers. No television. The windows
have bars on them like jail. I am in jail for what I did
to Jessica.

Then I went to see Dr Nevele.

His office is that way, go down this hall and go
20 through the big doors and then go this way and then
that's where. He has hair up his nose, it looks like SOS

---

2 **Children's Trust Residence Center:** Heim für geistig behinderte oder
  verhaltensauffällige Kinder.
10 **to ralph** (slang): kotzen.
11 **slacks** (pl.): sportliche Freizeithose.
12 **quiet:** *quietly.*
14 **wing:** (Gebäude-)Flügel, Teil, Abteilung.
15 **dresser:** Kommode.
21 f. **SOS pads** (pl.): Schwamm aus Stahlwolle.

pads. He told me to sit down. I did. I looked out the
window which doesn't have bars and Dr Nevele asked
me what I was looking at. I said birds. But I was looking for my dad to take me home.

5   There was a picture on Dr Nevele's desk of children
and there was a picture of Jesus Christ which is phony
I feel because they didn't have cameras then. He was
on the cross and somebody hung a sign over him. It
said INFO. That means you can ask him directions.

10   Dr Nevele sat down behind his desk. He said, "Now
why doesn't Burt tell me something about himself,
such as his most favorite things to do."

I folded my hands in my lap. Like a little gentleman.
I didn't say anything.

15   "Come on, Burt. What are your very favorite things
to do, say with some of your friends."

I sat. I didn't say any answer. He looked at me with
his eyes, and I looked out the window for my dad only
I couldn't see him. Dr Nevele asked me again and then
20   again and then he stopped asking. He waited for me to
talk. He waited and waited. But I wouldn't talk. He
stood up and walked around the room and then he
looked out the window too, so I stopped looking out it.

I said, "It's night."

25   Dr Nevele looked at me. "No it isn't, Burton. It's
day outside. It's the middle of the afternoon."

"It's night," I said. "When Blacky comes."

Dr Nevele looked at me. "Is the night named
Blacky?" he said.

30   (Outside the window a car parked and another car

6 **phony** (coll.): verlogen, unecht.

went away. My brother Jeffrey can name you any car, any car, man. He is an expert at cars. But when we ride in the back seat of our car we get yelled at due to horseplay.)

5 "At night Blacky comes to my house," I said, but I didn't say it to Dr Nevele. I said it to Jessica. "When I am tucked in tight. He stands outside my window and waits. He knows when. He is silence. He doesn't say any noise, not like other horses. But I know he is there
10 because I can hear him. He sounds like the wind. But he's not. He smells like oranges. Then I tie my sheets together and lower myself out the window. It is a hundred feet down. I live in a tower. It's the only tower on my block.

15 When I ride him his hooves make the sound like baseball cards in bicycle spokes and people think that that's what it is. But it isn't. It's me. And I ride Blacky out to where there's no more houses and no more people. Where there's no more school. To where they
20 have the jail where they keep people who didn't do anything wrong, and we stop next to the wall. It is silence. I stand on Blacky, he is very slippery but I never slip. And I climb over the wall.

Inside are soldiers, they have white belts criss-crossed
25 on them like safety boys only with beards. They are

---

3 **to yell at s.o.:** jdn. anschreien, laut ausschimpfen.
4 **horseplay:** Unsinn, Blödsinn.
7 **to tuck s.o. in tight** (coll.): jdn. ins Bett stecken, einmummeln.
16 **baseball cards:** Gemeint sind kleine Pappbilder von Baseball-Stars, wie sie in Kaugummipackungen enthalten sind.
spoke: (Fahrrad-)Speiche.
24 **criss-crossed:** über Kreuz, sich kreuzend.
25 **safety boys:** Schülerlotsen.

sweaty. They are sleeping. One of them is snoring, the fat one who is mean to children.

I sneak down to the jail part where the windows have bars on them and I whisper to the people inside, 'Are you innocent?' They say yes. So I unlock the bars with my pointer finger and let them out.

Just as I am climbing back over the wall the fat one who doesn't like children wakes up and sees me, but it is too late. I just wave at him and jump. It is a hundred feet down. Everybody thinks I am dead. But I'm not. I have a cape on and I hold it out like this and the wind comes and it fills up the cape and I like fly. I land on Blacky and then we go and have cookies and milk. I dunk them."

Dr Nevele stared at me. "That's very interesting," he said.

"I wasn't talking to you."

"Who were you talking to?"

"You know who."

"Who?"

(Outside a little boy like me played with a ball, he bounced it on the parking lot and laughed. His dad came and took him away from The Children's Trust Residence Center – home, where he played with trains that really go.)

---

1 **sweaty:** verschwitzt.
  to snore: schnarchen.
3 **to sneak:** schleichen.
11 **cape:** Umhang.
13 **cookie:** Keks.
14 **to dunk:** eintunken.
22 **to bounce:** (Ball) springen lassen.
  parking lot: Parkplatz.

"Burt, I want us to be pals. Pals that tell each other things. Because I think I can help you figure out what your problems are, and then help you solve them. You're a sick little boy. The sooner you let me help you the sooner you'll get better and go home. Help me, ok?"

I folded my hands up in my lap. It is correct for sitting. It is good citizenship. No talking, no gum. Dr Nevele stood in front of me and waited but I didn't say anything. I listened to the noise from out in the hall at The Children's Trust Residence Center, of children crying.

"I have to go now," I said.

"Why?"

"My dad is here."

"Burt, your parents have gone."

"No it's special, they came back to tell me something. They came back for me, Dr Nevele."

"Please sit down."

I was standing next to the door. I put my hand on the knob.

"Please sit down, Burt."

I watched him and I opened the door a little and he walked to me. I ran to the other side of his desk. He closed the door and stood in front of it.

"Burt, were you talking to Jessica?"

I didn't say anything.

"Jessica is not here," he said.

---

1 **pal** (coll.): Kumpel.
8 **it is good citizenship:** es gehört sich so, es ist manierlich.
  gum (coll.): Kaugummi.
21 **knob:** Türknopf, -knauf.

So I took the picture of Jesus Christ and threw it on the floor. I put the wastebasket on top of it and smashed it, then kicked it and ran to the corner by the window.

"She's in the hospital. Her mother was very upset. Very. Maybe you'd like to tell me your side of the story."

My throat started to hurt. It was killing me. I screamed "You shit ass" at him and made it hurt more, so I screamed it again and again. I screamed and screamed.

Dr Nevele walked to behind his desk. He didn't say anything and sat down and started reading a piece of paper like there wasn't anybody there. Only there was. There was a little boy in the corner. It was me.

"I have to call my dad," I said. "I just remembered I have to tell him something."

Dr Nevele shook his head without looking at me.

I walked over to his bookshelf. I leaned on it. It wobbled. I looked at Dr Nevele and said, "I wasn't talking to you," but he didn't look up. "I was talking to Jessica."

"Jessica is not here."

The books crashed down and went all over the room because I pushed the shelf over. The noise scared me. I ran to the door and opened it. Dr Nevele got up. I closed it.

Now he is going to knock some sense into me, I thought. He is going to teach me a lesson I'll never for-

---

9 **shit ass** (vulg.): Ober-, Blödarsch.
20 **to wobble:** wackeln.
28 **to knock some sense into s.o.:** jdm. Vernunft einbläuen.

get. He is going to show me who's boss around here. He is going to give me a taste of my own medicine. He is going to do it for my own good and I will thank him someday. And it will hurt him more than it does me.

5 But he didn't, he just looked at me. Then he said real quiet, "Do you want the seatbelt?"

I looked at him. He looked at me. We looked at each other.

"Yes."

10 I didn't know what it was. I watched him, he opened his drawer and took out a belt. He sat me down in the chair and put the belt around me and put the buckles in my hand. I have seen it before, like on airplanes, no holes. I pulled the belt around me. It was tight. I pulled
15 it more. Dr Nevele watched. It was around my stomach and I pulled it and then I pulled it down over my peenie and pulled it tighter and tighter on my peenie until it hurt me so much I started to cry, and I pulled it tighter. On my peenie.

20 "That's enough," said Dr Nevele. He came over and undid the belt and took it away. He picked up the telephone and dialed but it wasn't enough numbers. He said, "Send Mrs Cochrane down to my office." Then he walked over and crouched down in front of me and
25 looked at my face.

"Tell me one thing about her, Burt, just one thing and you can go back to your wing. When was the first time you saw her?"

I looked at him for a long time. Then I said some-
30 thing.

---

12 **buckle:** Schnalle.
17 **peenie** (coll.): Pimmel (*to pee:* pinkeln).

"There is a lawn in front of my house, and I am not allowed to walk on it because my dad pays a gardener good money, but sometimes I look at it from the driveway. Then clouds come. I stand on the driveway and I wait. Then the wind comes like it's going to rain. But it's not. The wind blows. It blows and blows and soon I can hardly stand.

So I start. I walk backwards ten steps and then I run down the driveway and jump. Then I run up the driveway and jump. Then I run down the driveway and jump and then the wind comes under me and lifts me up over the lawn and down the block over all the lawns that I am not allowed to walk on. I fly to Shrubs' house on the corner. The wind is always warm. In winter it is cold, but I can walk on the lawn then because there's snow."

Dr Nevele was leaning on the door. He frowned.

"Burton, the sooner you decide to help me, the sooner you'll be well enough to go home."

"Shut up," I said.

"What was that?"

"I wasn't talking to you."

"Who –"

"Jessica."

"I've told you, Jessica is not –"

I threw the chair at his face. He knocked it away, it ripped his sleeve and he ran up at me and grabbed me and squeezed me real hard but I yelled, "You're tickling me, you're tickling me."

3f. **driveway:** Hofeinfahrt.
17 **to frown:** die Stirn runzeln, das Gesicht verziehen.
27 **to rip:** aufschlitzen.
28f. **to tickle:** kitzeln.

The door opened. It was Mrs Cochrane. She was calm.

"Take Mr Rembrandt to the Quiet Room," said Dr Nevele, "until he regains control of himself. Do you want some help?"

Mrs Cochrane went out and came back with a man in a blue shirt, he was an attendant at The Children's Trust Residence Center. Then Dr Nevele let go of me. I wiped my nose on my sleeve and Mrs Cochrane took my hand.

"Mrs Cochrane, I can walk by myself you know," I said.

She laughed like. "Well just hold my hand anyway," she said. I said ok.

And now I am in the Quiet Room. There isn't any furniture in here except a chair. It is square in here. Four sides the same size. A square. It is geometry. I learned it in Homeroom at school. (At the Science Fair I saw a room with one wall, just. It was a circle.)

I deduce that it is raining outside. It is raining bow-wows and meows, like how Jeffrey said. (He is my brother, he can name you any car. Any, man.) I can tell it is raining because there is water running down my words where I am writing on the wall. Whoever made the Quiet Room made bad rooms. I deduce he was not ept.

---

7 **attendant:** Pfleger, Aufseher.
8 **to let go of s.o.:** jdn. loslassen.
18 **homeroom** (AE): (Schul-)Unterricht; (Schul-)Klasse.
   Science Fair: Technikmesse.
20 **to deduce:** schließen, schlussfolgern.
20f. **It is raining bowwows and meows:** kindersprachliche Variante zu *It is raining cats and dogs.*
26 **ept:** fähig, kompetent.

Raining. R A I N I N G. Raining.

On the way here I found a pencil in the hall. Mrs Cochrane didn't see me pick it up. And after she put me in here I did something. I climbed on the chair next to the wall. And wrote something with my pencil.

`When I was five I killed myself.`

I wrote it on the wall of the Quiet Room. I am writing now.

3

The first time I saw Jessica Renton was during the Air Raid Drill. It was near the end of last semester, in Spring. It was warm outside when we went to the main
5 part of school from the portable. The portable is a little house like, behind school, where the second grade is. I was in the second grade then.

(The portable smells an odor, I don't enjoy it as an aroma. The portable is very little for a building. There
10 are only two rooms in it. It was in one. Jessica was in the other one. I never noticed her until the Air Raid Drill.)

Air Raid Drill is ten short bells. It is very scary for children. There are rules. You have to line up in two
15 lines. You have to pull down the shades so the Russians won't know we're there and kill us. Then you have to pass quietly to the main part of school. Then you have to line up next to the lockers in the hall and sit down on the floor and turn off all the lights and sing
20 "God Bless America." It is very frightening.

2f. **air raid drill:** Fliegeralarmübung.
3 **semester:** Schulhalbjahr.
5 **portable:** hier: Pavillon, Nebengebäude.
6f. **second grade** (AE): zweite Klasse; Grundschüler der zweiten Klasse, i.a. 7 Jahre alt.
8 **to smell an odor** (coll.): miefen.
13 **scary** (coll.): schrecklich.
15 **shade:** Rollo.

Both the second-grade classes were in line outside
the portable waiting to go in the main part. There
wasn't any talking. (That is another rule.) Everyone
was scared because maybe there was going to be
5 bombs. I was scared only nobody knew. I am a good
actor, I feel.

Then somebody talked.

"I'm going home now, Miss Young."

It was a girl. She had brown hair, no braids (bar-
10 rettes, though). She stood just, with her hands behind
her back like she was ice skating.

"I just thought I'd tell you," she said. "Because I'm
going home now."

Miss Young said, "Jessica, please get back in line
15 now, there's no talking during an Air Raid Drill."

"No," said Jessica. "I'm going home," and she
started to walk away. Miss Young was very cross. She
yelled, "Jessica, come back here this instant!" Jessica
stopped and turned around. She came back and
20 walked up to Miss Young and said something very
quiet. "Miss Young, if there are going to be bombs I
want to be home with my family. That's where I'm
going."

Miss Young stood just. She didn't say any words.
25 Jessica looked up at her. She had a red dress on which
was soft, you could tell by looking at it. (I am good at
looking. I feel Jessica's dress was quite soft.)

Miss Young looked at Jessica.

---

9 **braid:** Zopf.
9 f. **barrette** (AE): Haarspange.
10 **to stand just:** etwa: bewegungslos dastehen.
17 **cross:** mürrisch, schlecht gelaunt, böse.

"This isn't an Air Raid," she said. "This is only a drill, a practice. There aren't going to be any bombs. It will be over in a few minutes, so there's no need to go home. Please get back in line."

Jessica didn't move even at all. I thought she was going to cry or something but she didn't. She talked without moving.

"Miss Young, you know I was very frightened because I thought it was dangerous. My dad is going to build a shelter in our cellar. He saw it in a magazine. I thought this was a real Air Raid. I don't think it's fair to scare children."

Miss Young didn't say a reply, but Jessica stood in front of her for a long time, and when the bells rang for the end of Air Raid Drill she was still standing there. I watched her. She stood until everyone was gone. She was all by herself. Then real slow she picked up the end of her dress, held it in her hands and twirled around and bowed.

This was the first time I ever saw Jessica Renton.

---

19 **to twirl around:** herumwirbeln, sich um die eigene Achse drehen.

4

That day I took Marlowe home from school. Usually I
walk down Lauder, the street I live on, but that day I
walked down Marlowe.

5   I waited by myself on the corner. (Usually I walk
home with Shrubs but he had to stay after school for
saying shit to Miss Filmer. Shrubs' real name is Kenny.
He is bad in school, all the teachers hate him. But he is
my best friend. I have known him since I was born. He is
10   exactly one week older than me. Exactly. We are blood
brothers. When we were five we pricked our fingers with
a pin and held them together. Except I didn't because I
am scared of pins. So I slammed my thumb in a drawer
to get blood. I had a cast for six weeks.)

15   I started to walk down Lauder first, but there were
the safety boys on the corner who are mean. They are
grease. They pick on little children. Which I am one. I
had my picture in my hand from school (we had color-
ing in Homeroom because we ran out of things to do)
20   and I waited on the corner for the safety to say, "Let's
go." Safeties stand with their arms out like this and say
"Hold it" when there are cars coming and then they
say "Let's go" when it is safe. This is why they are
called safeties.

---

13   **to slam:** hier: (ein)quetschen.
17   **grease** (slang): Rocker.
     to pick on s.o.: jdn. ärgern, hänseln.
22   **hold it!:** Stopp!

While I was waiting the safety saw my picture.

"What is that, a frog?"

"No," I said. "It's a horse, I drew it."

He looked at me, he was very large.

5   "What are you, stupid or something?" he said.

I said, "Yes." He was going to pound me. But my picture was quite good I feel, as a horse. It was green. I named him Greeny.

The safety grabbed it out of my hands, which ripped
10 Greeny's mouth. He laughed and showed it to the other safety who told him to quit screwing around. (They have two safeties on the corners so they can gang up on little children.) Then he gave Greeny back and said, "Let's go."

15   But I didn't. I said, "Do you have some Scotch tape to fix Greeny's mouth?"

"Are you kidding?" said the safety.

"You ripped it."

"Go piss up a rope," he said and made a fist at me
20 and I saw his fingernails were dirty.

This is why I walked home down Marlowe that day all by myself. I crossed the first street alone. First you stop. Then you look both ways to make sure no cars are coming. Then you walk don't run across the street.
25 I am good at safety rules. I have never got run over.

On Marlowe the trees had helicopters in them,

---

6 **to pound s.o.:** jdn. verhauen, jdm. einen heftigen Schlag versetzen.
11 **to screw around:** hier: Blödsinn treiben.
13 **to gang up on s.o.** (coll.): jdn. schikanieren, triezen.
15 **Scotch tape:** Tesafilm.
16 **to fix:** reparieren.
19 **go piss up a rope** (vulg.): verpiss dich, mach 'ne Fliege.

which are green things that twirl when they fall. I feel they are interesting as nature items.

Then something happened. I saw Jessica walking on the other side of the street with Marcie Kane who I
5 have no use for, to be candid, because she is a pig, no lie. Also she is Jessica's best friend I found out later. They didn't see me. I was invisible. But I slowed down and bent over to tie my shoe. (Only I didn't really because I have loafers which are cool, man. I made my
10 mom buy them for me. Usually she buys me Boy Scout shoes which I hate but I threw a conniption fit in the shoe store and she bought me the loafers I wanted. They don't have any sewing on them, none. None. They are pointy too. My mother cries every time she
15 sees them. She says, "To be candid, it makes me ashamed." This is where I got To be candid.)

Jessica and Marcie Kane walked down Marlowe. I watched them. They talked. Jessica was swinging a purse with fringe on it. I didn't know what was inside.
20 It swung up and down up and down against her dress and when it hit her, her dress got like waves in it. I thought, Inside the purse is a magic wand that turns into flowers. And you get a hat with it free, I seen one at Maxwell's.

---

2 **item:** Sache, Gegenstand, Ding.
5 **to be candid:** um ehrlich zu sein.
7 **invisible:** unsichtbar.
9 **loafers** (coll.): sportliche Halbschuhe (ohne Schnürsenkel), Slipper.
11 **to throw a conniption fit** (AE): einen Tobsuchtsanfall bekommen.
14 **pointy:** spitz (zulaufend).
19 **fringe:** Franse(n).
22 **magic wand:** Zauberstab.
24 **Maxwell's:** Supermarktkette.

Jessica's house was the one with blue shutters. Bricks not wood. Not red bricks though, mauve. She went in it is how I knew. She went in the side door from the driveway. Her driveway has grass down the middle which I don't like as much as our driveway which is plain. Also we have a back door, not side.

(Marcie Kane walked down Margarita. She lives on Strathmoor. In a toilet.)

I stopped across the street from Jessica's house and looked at it. I stood behind a little tree. (We have a little tree in front of our house, it still has paper wrapped around it from the tree store. This is how I can tell my house. When it is big I will be grown. But I will be able to tell my house from the fort on the front lawn. Which I will build when I get out of here. I built one once before, with Shrubs though, out of mud. My father had a conniption fit because he had to rent a truck to get the mud off the front lawn. It was a big fort. It was going to be mauve.)

There was wind on Marlowe, it messed my hair up. I combed it with my fingers. I have a princeton but I want a flat top like on "Spin and Marty," but my mom makes me get a princeton. I hate it. I would like to kill it. But when it gets long in front I can put Olivo Pomade on it, I dip the comb right in it. It is cool, man.

---

1 **shutter:** Fensterladen.
2 **mauve:** malvenfarben, hellviolett.
21 **princeton:** Topfschnitt (Frisur).
22 **flat top like on "Spin and Marty":** Bart-Simpson-Schnitt (*flat top:* oben gerade geschnittener Bürstenschnitt).
24f. **Olivo Pomade:** Markenname einer Haarpomade.
25 **to dip s.th. in:** etwas eintauchen.

(I got conniption fit from my mom. She said I had one.)

There were drapes on Jessica's windows. I looked at them for a half an hour. I could tell time because I had
5 my watch which I got for Hanukah until I lost it.

While I was looking at Jessica's drapes the sidewalk opened up under my feet. Luckily I didn't fall because my loafers have things so I can't fall. It was a hundred feet down and there were dinosaurs and fire. I jumped
10 over it and landed on the grass. Then I looked across the street and I saw Jessica had seen me and she said, "My, what a brave young man."

When I got home my mom asked me why I was late. I said I was in a car accident. She screamed. But I told
15 her it was ok because I didn't get killed, only some-body else did. She started yelling but I said I forgot who. Then I went up to my room and played with my men.

"Dad, how much are blue shutters?" I asked at
20 dinner.

"Why?"

"I'm going to put them on my fort."

"You're not building another fort while I'm alive."

"Ok," I said. "But how much are they, for when
25 you're dead?"

Later he said he'd get them wholesale but I don't

---

3 **drape:** Gardine.
5 **Hanukah:** Chanukka (jüdisches »Lichterfest«, das im Dezember gefeiert wird).
12 **my:** Ausruf; etwa: Mann!
18 **men:** Spielzeugfiguren.
26 **wholesale:** im Großhandel.

know what that means. I think it's when they bring them on boats.

Mauve. MAUVE. Mauve.

And in a few days school was over for summer vacation. Everyone said "Hooray." During the summer I played with Shrubs quite frequent. We played Zorro, he was the horse. I taught him how to neigh. It is like coughing only longer. I rode him. Our maid Sophie said I was going to cripple Shrubs. She is a colored negro.

I have a Zorro suit. Also I have Robin Hood and Peter Pan (which have the same pants) and Tom Corbett Space Cadet and Santa Claus and Superman and Doctor. When I play Zorro alone I use bolsters for the horse, I get them off my mom's bed and also I use them for bad guys to sock them. In Zorro the bad guy is El Commandante. He is on tv. Last month they got a different one. Jeffrey said he saw the old El Commandante on a Brylcreem commercial but he is lying, man.

Shrubs and me made a plan. It was a signal. It was whistling, like birds. The plan was that when Shrubs went to bed he was supposed to tie his sheets together

---

6 **Zorro:** schwarz gewandeter Held mit schwarzem Hut und Maske einer Reihe von Filmen gleichen Namens.

7 **to neigh:** wiehern (Pferd).

9 **to cripple s.o.:** jdn. zum Krüppel machen.

12 **Peter Pan:** Held aus dem gleichnamigen Kindermärchen und Zeichentrickfilm von Walt Disney.

12 f. **Tom Corbett Space Cadet:** etwa: Mr. Spock aus *Raumschiff Enterprise.*

14 **bolster:** (Kopf-)Polster.

16 **bad guys:** Schurken.

to sock (coll.): verprügeln.

19 **Brylcreem:** *Brylcream:* Markenname einer Haarpomade.

and lower himself out the window, then come to my house and give the signal and then I would tie my sheets together and lower myself out the window and then we would play Zorro at night, like real.

5 My bedtime is nine but I can stay up later if I throw a tantrum, but that night I went quietly. Usually Mom tucks us in. Sometimes she sings to us. She is very excellent as a singer. Jeffrey's favorite song is "Shine On Harvest Moon." Mine is "Hound Dog," only Mom
10 doesn't know it. Sometimes she doesn't tuck us in and I have to turn my light off by myself. I stand at the switch and point my finger at the bed, then I turn the light off and run where my finger goes. This is how I find my bed in the dark. I am scared of going to bed be-
15 cause there are monsters in my closet. I keep the door closed. The more times you push it the more closed it is. Before bed I push my closet door fifty times.

The night of our plan I had to take a bath before bed. I wish I was old enough to take a shower but I'm
20 not because I can't work it. Sometimes I take a shower with my dad. He is undressed and has hair on him and on his peenie. I don't have any on mine. I don't like to take showers with my dad.

Mom also reads to us before bed. My favorite book
25 is *The Puppy Who Wanted a Boy*. It is delightful. Jeffrey's favorite is *The Rickety Rackity Schoolbus*. Some-

---

5f. **to throw a tantrum** (coll.): einen Aufstand machen, einen Anfall bekommen.
9 **Hound Dog:** Erfolgstitel von Elvis Presley.
15 **closet:** Wandschrank.
25 **puppy:** Welpe, junger Hund.
26 **rickety rackity:** klapprig (Auto).

times Mom makes up stories and sometimes she makes
up more songs. She invented one entitled "All the Kids
in the Neighborhood." It is about bedtime on Lauder.
It has all their names and then it goes

5   And they're asleep are you
       Shhh Shhh Shhh Shhh
       And they're asleep are you.

It scares me to death.

That night we sat on my bed and Mom got out a
10 book. But it was different.

"Tonight we're going to have a special story," she
said. "Your father and I feel it's time you boys learned
some things about growing up. This book is called
From Little Acorns. Soon you'll be young men, and it's
15 time you knew."

"How come I'm a young man when I was a little
baby yesterday when I tracked in dirt?" I said.

She turned over the book which wasn't even in
color.

20 "Are there going to be dogs, Mom?" I asked. I
thought maybe there was going to be dogs.

"No, Honey," she said. "This is a story about real
people like you and Jeffrey and Daddy and me."

"Boring," said Jeffrey and he did this with his eye-
25 balls, and Mom said, "Keep it up, you'll be blind someday."

---

2 **entitled:** mit dem Titel.
14 **acorn:** Eichel.
17 **to track in dirt:** (mit den Schuhen) Dreck ins Haus tragen.
25 **keep it up!:** mach nur so weiter!

From Little Acorns was about some children whose mother was going to have a baby and they are on a farm with their grandfather who shows them chickens and eggs and everything. It was boring as H. I was nervous because I knew Shrubs was coming, for our plan.

Finally she stopped reading and went and then I put my Zorro suit on under the covers. I donned it. Then I waited. I waited and waited. It was hot in bed in my Zorro suit. Then I heard Shrubs outside yelling, "Burt!" I got out of bed. I started to tie my sheets together. Then the lights went on. It was my mother.

"Burt, Kenneth is here, he was outside calling for you, he says that you and he had arranged to play outside tonight. That's out of the question." Then she looked at me. I had on my Zorro suit. "Well, I suppose it's all right this once. Jeffrey will go with you. Look what you've done to my clean linens."

She took me downstairs. All the lights were on. My dad was watching tv. I had my mask and Zorro hat and Mom took the mask and said, "Here let me help you with this so it's straight." She said, "You can stay out fifteen minutes."

We went. First I ran behind a tree and ducked down. I watched out for El Commandante. He is very clever, Señor. He was on Seven Mile Road at the A&P with prisoners that I was going to rescue, so I hid behind a tree waiting for my horse so I could ride out of the

---

4 **boring as H** (coll.): stinklangweilig.
8 **to don:** (Kleidung) anlegen.
18 **linens** (pl.): Bettzeug.
24 **to duck down:** sich ducken, hinkauern.

30

night when the full moon is bright. I was going to rescue Jessica who was in jail for having blue shutters
which aren't allowed. I heard El Commandante. I took
out my sword.

5 "What are you doing with that pencil, Burt?" said
Jeffrey. "That's mine, it was on my desk."

He was telling Shrubs about his new model, it was a
Thunderbird. Shrubs asked him how many parts and
Jeffrey said a thousand, it was for big kids only. Shrubs
10 asked if he could watch Jeffrey put it together and Jeffrey said no because he would wreck it.

I was the only one playing Zorro.

I yelled out, "Come amigos, we go!"

Jeffrey said, "What are you talking about? Hurry up
15 and finish so we can get back."

We went around the block once then, just walking.
Then we went home. My mom asked if we had fun, but
I just went up to my room and pointed my finger at my
bed. I turned the light out by myself.

---

8 **Thunderbird: 1.** Kampfflugzeugtyp; **2.** Autotyp.
13 **amigos** (Span.): Freunde.

5

Z
Z

Last night was my second night at The Children's Trust
Residence Center. I threw up next to my bed.

It started when I had my appointment with Dr
Nevele yesterday. He knew I am writing on the Quiet
Room wall but he told me I am allowed. He said,
"Maybe Burton can express himself better in writing
than he can verbally." I don't know what verbally is. I
think it is some kind of vegetables.

At home I am not allowed to write on the walls, if I
do I get it. But once I drew a horse on my bedroom
wall and got spanked for it. I was just on the mane
when Mom walked into the room. She screamed.

"What do you think they make paper for, young
man?"

I said, "Airplanes, what else?" So she smacked me.
She said, "Who do you think you're talking to, one of
your friends?" And I said, "I thought you were."

"Wash it off, mister."

"No."

---

5 **to throw up:** sich übergeben, erbrechen.
13 **to get it** (coll.): Prügel kriegen.
14 **to get spanked:** Dresche kriegen.
    mane: Mähne (Pferd).
18 **to smack s.o.** (coll.): jdm. eine verpassen.

"Wash it off."

"No, it's my room and I can draw if I want."

She said, "It isn't your room, who do you think pays for it?"

5 "Who?"

"Your father."

"I'll pay him for it then."

"How?"

"I'll get a job."

10 "Doing what?"

"Selling stuff."

"Like what?"

"Lemonade."

I had to wash it off. It took all day, I used Bab-o.

15 At my appointment Dr Nevele made me sit in the same chair where I had the seatbelt before. He smiled at me but it was phony baloney, he made me sit there for a long time without saying anything. Then he did.

"Tell me about school, Burt."

20 I looked at the carpet in his office, it is brown with little lumps in it and I thought, Those are the buildings of the city down below where criminals lurk on every corner to steal things from innocent people. Up here in the sky I can use my x-ray eyes to see them and swoop

25 down to make them give it back.

Dr Nevele looked at me.

---

14 **Bab-o:** Produktname für ein Scheuermittel.

17 **phony baloney** (coll.): äußerst künstlich *(baloney* [slang]: Stuss, Quatsch*)*.

22 **to lurk:** lauern.

24 **x-ray eyes:** Röntgenaugen.

24f. **to swoop down:** herunterstoßen (Vogel).

"Who are your favorite teachers, Burton? You must have a favorite."

A little girl was standing on the roof of one of the buildings down below and a robber was chasing her around. I yelled, "Don't worry I'll save you!" and got off my chair and swooped down through the clouds and socked him and saved her. She had on a red dress with like waves in it.

"Please sit, Burton. A chair is to sit in, not climb on. You wouldn't do that at home," said Dr Nevele.

"I wasn't talking to you," I said.

"She's not here," he said and shook his head, and I kicked over the chair and it fell against the table and made the lamp tip over and it fell and the bulb exploded. Dr Nevele didn't say anything except, "What's your favorite class in school?"

Then out in the hall I heard wheels and I thought, There is a wagon with hay in it and inside is Shrubs only no one can see and he will jump out and throw me my sword and I'll point it at Dr Nevele and throw my head back and laugh and ride away. And I ran out into the hall, but I didn't see Shrubs. It was a wheelchair with a child in it with hardly any hair and her hands were like claws. I walked back into Dr Nevele's office and sat down. He didn't say anything to me.

"Can I have the seatbelt?" I said.

"Pardon me?"

"May I have the seatbelt?"

---

4 **to chase:** jagen.
18 **hay:** Heu.
22 f. **wheelchair:** Rollstuhl.
24 **claw:** Klaue.

Dr Nevele shook his head slow, like my dad did once when he had to put our dog to sleep.

"Please don't put me to sleep," I whispered.

I looked at the floor but there weren't any more buildings on it, just carpet. Dr Nevele shook his head. "Are you talking to me now, Burton?" he said. And I said, "I don't know." Then I started to cry.

He wrote something in his book for a long time and I just sat. Then he closed the book and said if I wanted to I could go to the Quiet Room and write things, if I didn't want to talk about them.

He stared at me for a long time then. He tried to smile at me. He tried and tried. I saw him trying. It made me sad. Dr Nevele was trying so hard to smile at me. He didn't know how.

I went to the Playroom instead. It is a room, it has toys in it for playing, there is even a little jungle jim made out of plastic which is good for climbing on and playing Tarzan. I am good at Tarzan, I can give the call.

There is a little square cut in the door of the Play-room so you can look inside from the hall. I did. There were children falling off the jungle jim who hit their heads, and other children running around like spazzes. I deduced they are mental. And there was a man with them who had red hair and white shoes like a doctor. I looked at him through the square. He was like the doctor of the spaz children. Suddenly he came toward me

---

17 **jungle jim:** Klettergerüst für Kinder.
19 f. **to give the call:** den Tarzanruf ausstoßen.
24 **spaz** (coll.): Spasti.
25 **mental** (coll.): geistig behindert.

and opened the door and looked at me and said, "Keep an eye on them will you, till I get back?"

One little boy sat by himself in the corner of the Playroom, because no one would play with him. He was a colored negro. He put his fingers up to his eyes and wiggled them like he was waving goodbye to himself. He rocked on the floor back and forth back and forth. Over and over. And over.

"Any trouble?" It was the red-haired man, he came back.

At first I didn't say anything but he looked at me with his eyes and they were brown with green pieces in them, like Jessica's.

"There's a little boy in there," I said, "who is waving goodbye to himself."

The red-haired man looked at me. He held out his hand. "Name's Rudyard," he said. But I didn't shake his hand. I didn't want to. I was scared. "Actually," he said, "he's waving hello." And he went back in the Playroom.

I went back to my wing. I was sleepy. I sat on my bed. It has sheets. At home is blankee. He is blue. I have had him since I was a baby. My mom wants to throw him away but I won't let her. But one time I did something. I peed on blankee. He smelled very pungent.

My bed is in the middle of the row. There are six beds in my wing and four other children. I don't know their names yet, except one. His name is Howie, he

---

6 **to wiggle s.th.:** mit etwas wackeln.
22 **blankee:** etwa: Wolldeck, Wolldecki.
25 f. **pungent:** stechend, durchdringend.

sleeps next to me, he has scars on him from when he threw a can of gas into a fire. He is mean. I asked him if they had hot dogs at The Children's Trust Residence Center and he told me to blow it out my ass hole. (This is swearing.) The bed next to me on the other side is empty. Maybe a little boy will come and sleep there and be my friend.

I sat on my bed and then I started to cry because I wanted to go home, so I pushed my face into my pillow and pushed and pushed until I fell asleep. I had a dream.

It was my house only not. We were in the den watching Popeye on tv, my mom and dad and Jeffrey. Then a man came on with a special announcement that there was going to be a tornado. I jumped up and yelled, "Come on everybody, quick, down into the cellar for shelter." But no one moved. Mom laughed at me and said, "Don't be such a little baby, Burt." Jeffrey was on the floor. He was looking at cars in a magazine. He said I couldn't look. I looked out the window and saw the sky was black and I yelled, "Hurry up!" But nobody moved. They acted like I wasn't even there. They talked to each other. My mom said, "Now no horseplay," and my dad looked at me and said, "Burt, did you take your bath? No bath, no Zorro on television." Behind him, through the window then I saw the tornado coming, it was long and black and squirmed so I couldn't tell which way it was going. I ran downstairs

---

4 **blow it out your ass hole!** (vulg.): steck's dir in den Arsch!
12 **it was my house only not** (coll.): es war mein Haus, bloß anders.
   den: Wohnzimmer (mit Fernsehgerät) (AE).
27 **to squirm:** herumwirbeln.

to the basement. I sat under the stairs and listened for
them to come down, but I couldn't hear anything except the tornado. It sounded like a train, so loud it hurt
my ears. It got louder and louder. It was coming at our
5 house. And I screamed, "Please you guys, please hurry
up." I screamed so loud I got sick until I couldn't hear
myself anymore. Everything started shaking. A glass
broke. Then I looked toward the door. There was Jessica, standing there and her lips were moving but I
10 couldn't hear. I said, "What?" but I couldn't hear. The
tornado roared like lions inside me, and then Jessica
turned and bowed and walked away. I ran after her,
but I was afraid to leave the cellar because of the tornado. I was scared. Chicken, man. I yelled and yelled.
15 Then Jessica turned around and looked at me, and
said, "Why did you do that to me, Burt, what you
did?" I started to cry. "Why did you do it?" she said,
and the tornado was inside me and I got down on my
knees and put my head against the floor and said,
20 "Please don't be dead, Jessica, please don't be dead."

When I woke up I didn't know where I was. I threw
up because I was so scared.

They had to get a janitor to clean it up this morning.
Howie said I am a baby for throwing up, and I didn't
25 know what to say back.

And today I had Dr Nevele again. I asked him if my
letter from Jessica got here yet. I told him on the night
we did it she said she would write me a letter if we
ever got separated.

30 "Don't count on it," said Dr Nevele.

---

14 **chicken** (coll.): feige.
23 **janitor:** Hausmeister.

I didn't talk to him after that. I folded my arms and sat. And talked to Jessica. And when he told me again that Jessica wasn't there I grabbed the papers on his desk and started to tear them up. But he just looked at me, and I didn't tear them.

"Go ahead," he said. "Or if you want them so badly, you can take them with you." I did.

I went to the Quiet Room. I am here now. I wrote something on the wall. Z. For Zorro.

(I got pungent from my dad. He said it about beets.)

Rembrandt, Burton (cont.)
12/3

Reticence continues as regards verbalized interaction with therapist. The patient will not speak directly to me, but favors a protracted form of verbalization. That is, communicating with me through the imaginary presence of the girl Jessica Renton (see file s7, item one). I judge this to be a function of two overlapping conditions: (a) The child unwilling to face the reality that Jessica has in fact been harmed by him and is at this writing being held for observa-

---

10 **beets** (pl.): rote Beete.
13 **reticence:** Reserviertheit, Distanziertheit.
   to verbalize: in Worten ausdrücken, in Worte fassen.
14 **interaction:** Umgang, Kommunikation.
16 **to protract:** hier: zeitlich verzögern, ausweichen.
17 **imaginary:** eingebildet, in der Fantasie vorhanden.
20 **to overlap:** sich überschneiden, überlagern.
23 **at this writing:** derzeit.
23f. **to be held for observation:** unter Beobachtung stehen.

tion at New Mercy Hospital (reports to be forwarded as per request 12/1), thus creating her fantasy presence here, unharmed; and (b) The child using this second person to speak to the therapist indirectly. Through this personality transference, he speaks to her and I hear it. It is my opinion that both conditions are at work here.

The fact remains, however, that for treatment to be effective in this case, direct verbal communication must be achieved. The issue of the wall-writing (see 12/2) proves the child to be language-oriented, indeed gifted (he is a spelling champion at school), and seems to be an appropriate avenue to explore.

The patient is displaying symptoms indicating a rescuer complex. This too serves a double function. (a) Displacement of guilt. Making oneself a hero by definition creates an external villain, thus displacing blame for bad deeds onto that villain and escaping

---

2 **to forward s.th.:** etwas weiterleiten.
  per request: auf Anforderung.
3 **unharmed:** unversehrt.
6 **personality transference**: Persönlichkeitsübertragung.
13 **language-oriented:** sprachlich orientiert, auf die Sprache ausgerichtet.
15f. **avenue** (fig.): Weg.
18 **rescuer complex:** Retterkomplex.
19 **displacement:** Verlagerung.
21 **external:** nach außen verlagert; hier: in Gestalt einer anderen Person.
  villain: Schurke, Bösewicht.

one's own guilt. And (b) Omnipotence. Sociopathology. The constant allusions to
flying, or jumping safely from high places,
sailing through the air. Putting oneself
5 above, and apart from, society. A symbolic
way of playing out his severe antisocial
tendencies.

At present this therapist judges the patient's uncontrollable temper to be the
10 severest and most immediate problem at
hand. It is pathological and inappropriate. He is a threat to those around him
and for that reason must be kept under
constant surveillance (at least kept with-
15 in the walls of this institution) and
given few privileges and no latitude in
which to display his violence.

I copied this on the wall from the papers I got from Dr
Nevele's office because I was bored, but I don't under-
20 stand it. It is too big words.

---

1 **omnipotence:** Allmacht, Allmächtigkeit.
1f. **sociopathology:** pathologisches Syndrom der gesellschaftlichen
Unangepasstheit.
2 **allusion:** Anspielung.
6f. **antisocial tendency:** gegen die Gesellschaft gerichtete Neigung.
9 **uncontrollable:** unbeherrschbar.
temper: Wutausbruch.
10f. **at hand:** vorliegend.
11 **pathological:** pathologisch, krankhaft.
11f. **inappropriate:** unangemessen.
14 **surveillance:** genaue (ärztliche) Beobachtung.
16 **latitude:** Spielraum.

6

After summer vacation I had to go back to school. I
didn't want to. I had forgot about school because of
vacation, which is long when you're a child. I hate
school. You have to get up early. My mom wakes me
by coming into my room and patting my head and then
she pats my tushy (which is under blankee) and then
she gets real close to my face and whispers, "Burt,
Sweetheart, it's time to get up." She whispers soft and
nice. I could kill her. I wish I just had an alarm clock.

I get up. I go to the bathroom. I brush my teeth and
I wash my face and I make. (I like the upstairs bathroom best because it is blue, the downstairs is pink like
for girls.) Then I get dressed. I can dress myself. Mom
lays out my clothes the night before on the other bed
in my room where Jeffrey used to sleep except that
now he has his own room, where Sophie used to sleep
except that now she doesn't. I don't know where
Sophie sleeps. I don't think she does.

I hate my clothes, they are square. Larry Palmer has
cool clothes. They are sharp, man, he has chinos. His
hair goes down in front like on Brylcreem commer-
cials.

---

6 **to pat:** tätscheln; einen Klaps geben.
7 **tushy** (coll.): Po.
12 **to make** (coll.): sein (großes oder kleines) Geschäft machen.
20 **square:** spießig.
21 **sharp** (coll.): cool, geil.
  chinos (pl.): eine Art locker geschnittene Jeans.

When I am dressed I come down for breakfast which
Mom makes me and which I can't stand, to be candid,
because it makes me want to ralph my guts out. I am
never hungry for breakfast but she makes me eat it, it
5 is scrambled eggs with like water around the edge. My
mom sits in her chair where she always sits, at the end
of the table, turned sideways so she faces me. I sit in
Jeffrey's chair for breakfast because he goes earlier
than me. Mom wears her pink robe. She has a net on
10 her hair. She has slippers that hang off her feet so you
have to look at them. They have nail polish on her toes
that is all chipped and you have to look at her legs
which have veins in them which are blue. She smells
like lotion, you can smell it across the table. I have to
15 eat watery scrambled eggs and smell her lotion.

At breakfast everything is very silence because it is
early in the morning. I can hear the clock in the living
room. It says tick tock. My mom always has a cup of
coffee. She stares at the wall. She zups it. Then she
20 holds it in her mouth for an hour. I wait. Everything is
quiet. Tick tock. I wait. Then she swallows it. It sounds
like a tidal wave. Then she gives me my lunch to take.
It is in a bag which is brown. It is a new bag. I have a
new bag every day. She folds it over three times and

---

3 **to ralph one's guts out** (vulg.): sich auskotzen.
5 **scrambled eggs** (pl.): Rührei.
7 **sideways** (adv.): zur Seite hin.
9 **robe:** Bade-, Morgenmantel.
10 **slippers:** Pantoffeln.
11 **nail polish:** Nagellack.
12 **chipped:** abgeplatzt, abgebröckelt.
19 **to zup:** (Getränk) schlürfen.
22 **tidal wave:** Flutwelle.

staples it. Some of the other children, like from the Home, bring bags that are all wrinkly. Some other children have lunch boxes with cartoons on them which I feel are for sissies.

5 I don't eat my lunch. I put it in my locker and leave it there to rot. The reason is that I have pleurodynia. It is a disease, my doctor says, when I have cramps and diarrhea. It is entitled pleurodynia. But I deduce that if I don't eat I won't get it, even though I am a big eater
10 and at home I am always a Clean Plate Commando.

At school you can buy lunch for thirty-five cents. You stand in line, the cooks are all fat and sweaty with nets on their hair and red fingers. You get milk in little bottles. It is warm, they keep it next to where they
15 have the rags that you use to clean up the tables when you're through. The water is gray with pieces of food floating in it. It smells like vomit. You wipe the tables off with the rag and it leaves white gunk. I don't buy milk at school very frequent.

20 Sometimes I am lunchroom captain for the day and I have to wash the table. You get to be tardy going back

---

1 **to staple s.th.:** etwas zutackern.
2 **Home:** Heim (öffentliche Einrichtung).
  wrinkly: zerknittert.
3 **cartoons:** Comics.
4 **sissy** (coll.): Waschlappen, Heulsuse.
6 **pleurodynia:** Pleurodynie (seitlicher Brust- und Rippenfellschmerz; Seitenstechen).
7 **cramps:** (Bauch-)Krämpfe.
8 **diarrhea:** Durchfall.
  to be entitled: heißen.
10 **Clean Plate Commando:** etwa: Tellerleerputz-Kommando.
18 **gunk** (coll.): Schmiere.
21 **tardy:** säumig.

to class. Once I used a big broom and swept off the table and Miss Shultz said she was going to brain me. (Miss Shultz is the gym teacher who is in charge of lunch because lunch is in the gym, they have tables that
5 go inside the walls like. Miss Shultz thinks she is a man. She wears sports jackets and she doesn't have any lips.)

The first day of school after summer vacation Shrubs called for me and then we went next door and called for Morty Nemsick, who is a spaz, I feel. Then we
10 walked to school. It is exactly three and a half blocks. Exactly.

We had an assembly first thing.

Assemblies are in the auditorium. Auditorium is also a class, I have it sometimes, you put on plays. Last
15 semester another class did *The Wonderful Wizard of Oz*. It won a prize. Auditorium is a special class. Usually you have Homeroom for half the day and special classes for the other half.

(I saw tidal waves once in a movie at assembly,
20 about an earthquake. Tidal waves are the large economy size.)

That first day we went to assembly right after reporting to our old rooms. For assembly you enter the auditorium in an orderly fashion, no talking, girls in one

---

2 **to brain s.o.** (coll.): jdn. verdreschen.

4f. **that go inside the walls like:** Gemeint ist: in die Wand versenkbar.

13 **auditorium:** Aula, Foyer.

15f. **"The Wonderful Wizard of Oz":** 1900 veröffentlichtes Kinderbuch von L. Frank Baum; davon liegen auch eine dramatisierte Fassung und ein Musical-Film vor.

16 **special class:** etwa: AG.

20f. **to be the large economy size** (coll.): gigantisch sein.

24 **orderly:** geordnet, ordentlich.

line boys in the other. You wait to be seated. Each class has a special place. I sat next to Shrubs so we could fool around. When we sat down he took out a pen he had, there was a picture of a girl on it that when you turned it upside down her dress fell off. He bought it for seventy-five cents off the safety on Seven Mile Road who is a hood. The pen gave me a funny feeling in my stomach, under my stomach. Everybody looked at it, we were in the middle of the row. Then Miss Filmer was coming so Shrubs put it under his shirt.

For assembly we had Officer Williams. We had him before, he is a fuzz. He has a gun and everything. We always say "Shoot Miss Filmer," but he never does. He is an artist. He has an easel and draws and tells stories at the same time. It is boring, man. He drew a traffic light, it was three circles. Then he told us we should be extra careful crossing in winter because the streets are slippery and then he changed the traffic light into a snowman. He drew a wise old owl and changed it into a bicycle but I don't know how because I was watching Shrubs turn his pen over.

But then something happened. Miss Filmer saw. Shrubs tried to hide it but it was too late. She leaned over four people and grabbed at the pen but Shrubs pulled it away and she fell on top of me. She was quite heavy for a teacher. She grabbed the pen.

"Where did you get this, mister?" she said.

"I don't know," said Shrubs. (Shrubs always says "I don't know" when he gets yelled at.)

---

7 **hood** (slang): Gangster.
12 **fuzz** (slang): Bulle.
14 **easel:** Staffelei.

"What do you mean you don't know?"

"I don't know."

Miss Filmer got very cross. "Answer me, young man!"

Shrubs said, "I don't know what I mean by I don't know."

"How come you never know anything?" asked Miss Filmer.

"I don't know," said Shrubs.

Miss Filmer tried to slap him but he ducked and she hit me instead. It didn't tickle. I tried to get up but she was still like on top of me and then she like fell on the floor and the pen dropped and rolled all the way to the front of the auditorium under the seats and everyone tried to grab it.

Officer Williams drew a railroad sign and turned it into a safety boy. (The R was a nose.)

Sylvia Grosbeck picked up the pen and gave it to Miss Filmer. Filmer put it in her pocket and went like this with her finger to Shrubs which means come here.

"Come and get me!" said Shrubs. (He was mad.)

She did.

Officer Williams looked over and it made him goof on the safety boy's face and Marty Polaski yelled out, "Oo, scarred for life!" So Miss Filmer grabbed him too and dragged them both to the back of the auditorium into her office. You could hear her yelling, and a little child in the front row started crying real loud and Officer Williams said a poem:

---

10 **to slap s.o.:** jdm. eine Ohrfeige geben.
23f. **to goof on s.th.** (coll.): etwas verpatzen, -pfuschen, -masseln.
25 **scarred for life:** etwa: (von einer Narbe) für's Leben gezeichnet.

Policemen are your friends when you get lost.
Safety boys are there to help you cross.
Traffic signals tell us stop and go.
These are safety rules that you should know.

5   Then the ball rang and everyone started making noise. Miss Krepnik said, "That was not a signal to talk." But nobody knew what to do because it was a new semester and nobody knew what class to go to. The teachers had a meeting in the front of the audi-
10 torium and all the children started to visit with their neighbors. I wondered where Shrubs was. I thought Miss Filmer killed him.

   Then Miss Murdock came. She was my first grade teacher. She said for everyone to go back to last year's
15 Homeroom and pass from there except for the following people and she read off names, and one of them was mine. Everyone else left. I started to sweat because I didn't see Shrubs. I thought Miss Filmer killed him. And I almost was crying. She came out of her of-
20 fice with her arms folded and suddenly I was standing up. And I walked to her across the front of the audi-torium, and I thought, I am on a mountain up high and down there is everyone, and there is wind blowing me. I stood in front of Miss Filmer and suddenly I was
25 screaming.

   "What did you do to Shrubs!" I screamed. "If you hurt him I'll kill you, I swear to God!" And then I wet my pants, and I started to cry real hard because I thought

10 **to visit with s.o.** (coll.): mit jdm. schwatzen.
15 **homeroom** (AE): Klassenzimmer.
27 **to wet:** nass machen.

everybody saw, and then the door to the auditorium opened and Jessica was standing there and she saw.

I cried and went and sat down. Auditorium was my next class, that's why Miss Murdock read my name.

5 Mr Stolmatsky came in. He is a teacher but also he is an actor at a college. He was in charge of *The Wonderful Wizard of Oz*, when they did it for the contest last semester. Then Miss Filmer made an announcement.

10 "Since almost the whole cast from the *Wizard of Oz* happens to be in this class, Mr Stolmatsky has asked if we could use this period to rehearse for the contest coming up in Lansing."

I sat alone.

15 Mr Stolmatsky said for the cast to get on stage. Jessica got up. She was Dorothy. She had the red dress on that had waves in it when she walked. Also there were three boys. They stood just. And there was another boy on the side of the stage who blew on his fist. Later 20 I found out it was supposed to be a microphone and he was the sound of the tornado. Mr Stolmatsky went to the back of the auditorium and shouted, "Ok, back on the boards, thespians." (I haven't the vaguest idea what this means.) Then Jessica was in the middle of the 25 stage. She started to say words.

She said, "Auntie M, Auntie M."

---

12 **contest:** Wettbewerb.
16 **Dorothy:** Figur aus *The Wonderful Wizard of Oz*.
21 **tornado:** Gemeint ist der Wirbelsturm zu Beginn von *The Wonderful Wizard of Oz*.
23 **thespians:** Mimen (*Thespis:* griechischer Tragödiendichter).
   I haven't the vaguest idea: ich habe nicht die leiseste Ahnung.
26 **Auntie M:** *Aunt Em:* Figur in *The Wonderful Wizard of Oz*.

It was very soft. Mr Stolmatsky said he couldn't hear but Jessica didn't listen to him because she was looking out someplace, I could see her eyes all the way from where I was. They were green with brown pieces in-
5 side. She stood for a long time just looking and every-body waited. Then very slow she started to get down on her knees. She got on her knees and whispered, "Auntie M, Auntie M."

The boy on the side of the stage stopped blowing on
10 his fist. Nobody moved. It was real silence. Jessica whispered, "Auntie M, Auntie M." Then she stopped. Her lips moved but there wasn't any words coming out. She layed down on the floor and put her head down on her arm.

15 "What's going on?" Mr Stolmatsky yelled. "Did you forget the rest of your lines?"

Jessica lifted her head up very slow, and I saw she was crying. Mr Stolmatsky was very surprised, he didn't say anything else, and I knew she didn't forget.
20 After a few seconds Mr Stolmatsky said, "That was excellent, Sweetheart, you really made us care about Dorothy."

Jessica looked at him for a long time.

"Shut up, Mr Stolmatsky," she said.

25 (I got I haven't the vaguest idea from my mother. She always says it when I ask her riddles from *My Weekly Reader*. My favorite is, "Why did the moron throw a clock out the window?")

---

26 **riddle:** Rätsel.
27 **moron** (coll.): Trottel, Idiot.

7

> He wanted to see time fly.

I didn't write this.

I have been at The Children's Trust Residence Center for a week now. I hate it. I would like to kill it. What I hate worst is breakfast. It is in a big noisy room with long tables where we eat with other youngsters who are sickening to look at.

Mrs Cochrane and the children from my wing sit at one table. There is Phil and Robert and Manny and Howie. Robert is only seven. Howie is nine and the rest are eight like me. Robert cries all the time which makes me nervous, to be candid, and he wets his bed at night and it smells quite pungent. He sleeps across the aisle from me. Next to me sleeps Howie, the boy with the scars. Phil never talks, he is silence and just smiles all the time and I don't know why, but maybe he is happy happy or maybe his face is froze that way. (My mom says when I frown my face will freeze that way and I say "I'm glad so then I won't have to frown anymore, my face will do it all by itself.") Manny is my age, he is also Jewish like me, he has black curly hair and says oy all the time.

At breakfast today I made a hippopotamus out of

---

8 **sickening:** Übelkeit verursachend, krank machend.
15 **aisle:** (Mittel-)Gang.
18 **froze:** *frozen.*
24 **hippopotamus:** Nilpferd.

my oatmeal, which was all dried up. I made a bed for
him out of cinnamon toast and I took my napkin and
made a blanket. Then I took my spoon and beat him to
death. I smashed his head open and broke him in half
and smeared him on the plate. Mrs Cochrane got cross,
she asked me why I did it. I said because he was a bad
hippopotamus because he killed Jessica. He dragged
her into the river and killed her. Robert said, What
river? I poured my orange juice over his head and said,
"This river."

I got marched right down to see Dr Nevele.

He still had his coat on, which surprised me because
I thought he lived at The Children's Trust Residence
Center but he doesn't. I think he lives in a shopping
center.

"Good morning, sir," he said to me, smiling. "Won't
you step into my chambers?"

I wouldn't. It was what he said. I wouldn't. I tried to
run away but Mrs Cochrane grabbed me.

"What is this all about?" said Dr Nevele.

Mrs Cochrane told him about breakfast.

"No," I said. "That's not it."

"Then what is it?"

"You know," I said.

"No I don't," said Dr Nevele. "I haven't a clue. Now
please come in here."

---

1 **oatmeal:** Hafermehl; hier: Haferbrei.
2 **cinnamon:** Zimt.
  napkin: Serviette.
5 **to smear:** schmieren.
11 **to march s.o.:** jdn. wegbringen, abführen.
17 **chambers:** Kabinett, Räumlichkeiten (*chamber:* Kammer).
25 **I haven't a clue:** ich habe keine Ahnung.

"I won't go to your chambers," I said.

"Burton."

"Don't," I said. "I'll be good from now on. Don't kill me. Don't kill me, Dr Nevele!"

5 "What? Why Burt, what makes you, please, Son."

And I was screaming. I tried to run but he held me and I kicked at him und bit him to get away. I had to get away.

"Mrs Cochrane, take him to the Quiet Room where
10 he'll feel safe."

I ran there. All by myself. Because Dr Nevele said chambers. Because when I was five I saw a movie, it gave me bad dreams which I still have them. It was a movie about a room where they torture you and have
15 a thing that goes over your stomach and squeezes you till your stomach squeezes out through holes like spaghetti, and you bleed to death, and there is a man in a black hood who is a doctor, like Dr Nevele. It was called *The Torture Chamber of Dr Night*.

20 There were legs in the Quiet Room. Imagine my surprise. It was the man with the red hair from the Playroom. He is like a doctor too. He was surprised when I walked in. I started to leave.

"Don't," he said. "Don't go. I was just leaving. I was
25 about to leave. Take over here, will you, stout fellow?"

He had on a tie this time, like dressed up. I stayed in the Quiet Room but he didn't leave. He just sat there.

"I'm going," he said. "Any minute." Then he did

18 **hood:** Kapuze.
25 **stout:** untersetzt, kräftig, stark.
26 **dressed up:** vornehm gekleidet.

something funny. He put his fingers up to his eyes and wiggled them, and he like hummed, only it was noise, not music.

"You shouldn't sit on the floor in your good clothes," I said. "You'll get punished."

He looked up at me. His eyes were green with brown pieces, like Jessica's.

"So true," he said. "And yet so far."

Then he stood up and left.

Then I went to write this on the Quiet Room wall and I saw somebody had wrote

        He wanted to see time fly.

And it wasn't me.

So I followed him because he shouldn't have wrote on my wall. He went down to the Playroom. The door was open. I watched him through the little window, he was in there with the little colored negro boy I saw before, the one who is spaz. The red-haired man was crawling on the floor with him, and the little boy was crying and crying. Then the red-haired man saw me. He stood up and told me to come in. I went in.

"This is Carl," he said to me. "He bites." And he walked out of the room and closed the door. And I was alone with Carl. Who bites.

He got up and suddenly started running all over the Playroom as fast as he could and smashed into the door and bounced off and walked away without crying or anything. Then he sat down. Then he got up. Then

---

2 **to hum:** summen.
11 **wrote:** *written.*
27 **to bounce off:** zurückprallen.

he made a circle and walked on some toys and sat
down again. I didn't say anything to him, I thought he
didn't know I was there even. He picked up a bean bag
and ate it. His eyes went funny. One over here and one
5 over here. He blinked and jerked his head. He started
to crush the toys in the toy box.

"You shouldn't," I said.

But all he did was whistle. Then he stood up and
walked into the wall and then he sat down against the
10 wall and put his hands up to his eyes and wiggled his
fingers. It was the same thing that the red-haired man
from the Quiet Room did.

Carl fell over and rolled on the floor and smashed
into the jungle jim and it almost crashed on him but it
15 didn't, so he sat with his back against the wall again
and started rocking and pounding the back of his head
against the wall. I could see there was a little bald spot
on the back of his hair from pounding. Suddenly he sat
up straight and put his hands in his lap and sat like a
20 little gentleman.

I said, "Your are sitting very nice, Carl, with good
citizenship."

He hummed, only noise, not music, like the red-
haired man did, and then he stood up and walked over
25 to a little red wagon they had in the Playroom and
climbed inside it and sat down with good citizenship.

"You aren't supposed to," I said. "It's for carrying
stuff in."

---

3 **bean bag:** mit Bohnen gefülltes Jutesäckchen (für Wurfspiele).
5 **to blink:** blinzeln.
　to jerk one's head: den Kopf hin und her werfen, ruckartige Bewe-
　gungen mit dem Kopf machen.
16 **to pound:** fest schlagen, hämmern.

But he stayed. He was like a statue in the little red wagon. (It had "Little Red Wagon" painted on the side of it.) I picked up a bean bag and threw it to him, but he didn't move and it hit his head.

5 "You're supposed to catch it and throw it back," I said. "You better get out before the red-haired man comes back or you'll get punished."

Then the door opened up and an attendant walked in. He took Carl's hand and tried to pull him out of the 10 little red wagon, but he wouldn't go.

"Come on, stop giving me such a hard time," said the attendant, who was large and hairy. Carl bit him on the hand. I could see it started bleeding, and the attendant yelled, "You little bastard," and grabbed Carl 15 around the shoulders so he couldn't move and twisted his arms around him. Carl screamed and kicked and bit his teeth in the air, and the attendant could hardly hold him. He let go.

"I'll be back," he said.

20 Carl stopped. He just stopped like a cartoon. Then he made a noise.

"Puss."

I went up to him. He sort of looked at me and I reached out my hand and he didn't even bite. I 25 touched him. He said, "Puss." Then he grabbed my hand and pulled me but I got away. Then he screamed real high like a siren and then I got real mad and yelled at him, "Shut up, Carl, don't you know they are coming back with seatbelts and they are going to pun- 30 ish you and slap you across the face and show you

27 **siren:** Sirene.

56

who's boss and for your own good! God damn you. I can't understand you."

And I cried too and I don't even know why, because it was Carl. He grabbed my hand and put it on the little red wagon.

"Puss."

The attendant came back in a few minutes with another man, only Carl wasn't in the little red wagon. He was sitting very good citizenship in a little chair by the window of the Playroom.

They looked at me.

I said, "All he wanted was for somebody to push him."

They took Carl away and I went back to the Quiet Room. I was thinking about the red-haired man who wiggled his fingers in front of his eyes and hummed noise like Carl. He was a doctor but he didn't act like a doctor. He acted like a little boy. Like me.

Rembrandt, Burton (cont.)
12/10

Interest in this case is now being shown by Rudyard Walton, first-year intern, working in the Upper South Program here, dealing primarily with autistic and mentally retarded children.

Walton's work, much praised thus far by his department, is supposedly of the

---

22 **first-year intern:** hier: anstaltsinterner Jungtherapeut.
24 **autistic:** autistisch, d.h. beziehungs- und kommunikationsunfähig.
24f. **mentally retarded:** geistig zurückgeblieben.
27 **supposedly** (adv.): vermutlich.

"wounded healer" type, dealing with the patient one-to-one, and actually assimilating that patient's symptoms himself, thus, I suppose, establishing an empathetic rela-
5 tionship.

He denies any therapeutic involvement in this case, insisting that he simply "likes" the child and enjoys his company. I nevertheless asked him to kindly restrict his work
10 to the Upper South Program.

Walton's intercourse with this patient may prove detrimental to the child's progress. Clearly, his technique is designed to first reinforce the existing behaviors of the
15 child, leaving modification until later, after a relationship has been established. While perhaps effective in cases of severe autism, such techniques are inappropriate to sociopathology.
20 For the purposes of record, I report that Mr Walton reportedly left one of his own patients, a severely autistic child named Carl, alone with Burton Rembrandt under no

---

2 **to assimilate s.th.:** etwas übernehmen.
4 **empathetic:** empathisch, mitfühlend.
6 **involvement:** Engagement.
11 **intercourse:** Umgang.
12 **to prove detrimental:** sich als abträglich erweisen.
13 **technique:** Methode, Vorgehen(sweise).
14 **to reinforce s.th.:** etwas verstärken.
15 **modification:** Veränderung.
20 **for the purposes of record:** etwa: der Vollständigkeit halber.
21 **reportedly** (adv.): angeblich.

58

supervision of any kind, and as a result of
this negligent behavior, an attendant was
seriously wounded by a bite from the child.
This is clearly against the policy of this
5 institution. (Walton later claimed that the
abandonment was intentional, and that both
children actually benefited. The matter,
however, comes up before the Board of Review
next week.)

10 Walton also mentioned that he feels the
Rembrandt case to be misplaced in this institution. He feels the child does not belong here. I maintain, however, that the
boy's behavior remains not only disturbed,
15 but recently he has manifested paranoid
schizophrenic symptoms involving halluci-
nations about killers in my office, clearly
guilt-generated as regards his actions with
the girl Jessica.

20 It is my firm judgment that the child is

---

1 **supervision:** Aufsicht.
2 **negligent:** nachlässig.
4 **policy:** Statuten, Bestimmungen.
6 **abandonment:** Verlassen; Vernachlässigung, Tatsache, Umstand,
   dass man jdn. sich selbst überlässt, unbeaufsichtigt lässt; Leichtfer-
   tigkeit, Nachlässigkeit.
   intentional: absichtlich, beabsichtigt.
8 **Board of Review:** Aufsichtsgremium (der Heimleitung).
11 **misplaced:** fehl am Platze.
15 **paranoid:** paranoid, wahnhaft.
16 **schizophrenic:** schizophren, mit gespaltener Persönlichkeit.
16f. **hallucination:** Wahnvorstellung.
18 **guilt-generated:** durch ein Schuldgefühl, schlechtes Gewissen er-
   zeugt, verursacht.

severely disturbed and must be kept here, probably for some time.

This was on a paper. I stole it from Dr Nevele, from his desk when I was there.

8

While I was sitting in the Quiet Room Mrs Cochrane came and told me that I had to go to the dentist tomorrow, that it is the rules of The Children's Trust
5 Residence Center. I grabbed her arm and bit her like Carl and she slapped me across the face so I started to scream as loud as I could, "I'm going to kill somebody I'm going to kill somebody!"

She left me in the Quiet Room alone. But when I go
10 to the dentist I am going to kill him. I hate the dentist. At home I have to go. Mom takes me.

The first thing when you walk in is the smell. I get sick at my stomach and it makes me afraid. When you open the inside door a bell rings. There is a window in
15 the wall that you can't see through and it has a nurse behind it and she slides it open and asks me my name. Then I sit down. Everything is silence except for the aquarium with bubbles in it. Music comes out of the ceiling. On the walls are pictures of children winking at
20 me all happy happy.

The door opens and the nurse says my name all smiley. I have to go in. I go in the room, it has water gurgling, and she sits me in the lay-down chair and pulls it backwards and puts a bib on me and a thing behind
25 my neck.

19 **to wink at s.o.:** jdm. zuzwinkern.
22 f. **to gurgle:** gurgeln, glucksen.
24 **bib:** Lätzchen.

The drill hangs over me, it has wires and wheels and hoses on it. It bends. There are different tips he puts in it. Each one is to hurt me.

Then I sit there and nothing happens but I hear a child next door screaming. Then the nurse comes in and says "Open." She talks very quiet. Everyone at the dentist talks very quiet, and it scares me to death. Then she sticks knives in my gums and scrapes my teeth.

Then Dr Stahl walks in very fast, he is in a big hurry and he pretends to be happy happy only I know he isn't because I kicked him in the balls once. That was when I was five. But I know you have to have good citizenship at the dentist. He has the drill and I don't. Dr Stahl looks at my paper then looks in my mouth then looks at my paper then looks in my mouth. He has a mirror on a stick and he looks in my mouth (I sometimes pretend I am him with a spoon but it makes you upside down) and I ask him if I have any cavities but all he says is "Open."

Then he takes out all his tools and makes noise on my teeth and says "Clickity clack on the railroad track." He is trying to be funny, but it isn't fun. He says "Let me know if I poke you," but I can't because his fist is in my mouth. Then he takes a sharp thing and

---

1 **drill:** Bohrer.
2 **hose:** Schlauch.
tip: (Bohr-)Aufsatz, (Bohrer-)Spitze.
12 **balls** (coll.): Hoden, ‚Eier‘.
18f. **it makes you upside down** (coll.): es würgt einen, es dreht einem den Magen um.
19 **cavity:** Loch im Zahn, Karies.
24 **to poke:** pieksen.

jams it in my tooth and wiggles it and I have like electricity going through me and I spin it hurts so bad.
Then he says "Now let's look at the downstairs."

He looks at my paper and makes some marks. I ask
5 him "Please, do I have any cavities, do I have to be
drilled?" And Dr Stahl says "Open."

He screws a metal thing on my mouth with cotton in
it and he puts the sucker under my tongue and it sucks
up my whole mouth and my tongue and he takes the
10 drill and puts it in my mouth and the noise starts like
jet planes taking off inside me and it gets very hot and
my head spins and it hurts so bad I think I am going
into the ground and he leans way over me and I look
in his face and he isn't smiling anymore. It hurts so
15 bad. I try and ask him to stop for only a second but I
can't because he is still drilling and if I move it will cut
open my tongue. I almost stand up it hurts so much,
and he holds me with his elbow. Then I hear a siren inside my head, on an ambulance coming for me. The
20 drill goes through my mouth into my head and up to
my eyes and my blood inside me is hurting. No one
will help me. No one will help me.

When I come out of the office my mom says "Now
see, that wasn't so bad was it?"

25 And last night at The Children's Trust Residence
Center I thought about the dentist and cried myself to
sleep, because I am afraid, and Mommy isn't here
even. I want to go home.

---

1 f. **electricity:** elektrischer Schlag.

2 **I spin:** mir dreht sich alles, mir ist schwindlig.

3 **downstairs** (coll.): hier: untere Zahnreihe.

8 **sucker:** Sauger, Speichelabsaugegerät.

And this morning instead of breakfast I went to the Playroom and looked out the window, because nobody was in there. I watched the traffic go by and wondered if anyone was going to my house. Then I heard the Playroom door open. But I didn't turn around. I didn't want to see anybody.

There wasn't any noise for a while, then I heard singing. It was a man. He sang, "I'll walk alone, because to tell you the truth I'll be lonely."

It was soft. I looked out the window. I didn't turn around. He sang some more. It was good singing.

(I am good in Music at school. Next semester I will be in Glee. Miss Allen promised. Once we had a song, "The Three Billy Goats Gruff," and Miss Allen chose three special boys to sing it for assembly. It was Kenny Aptekar, Gary Faigin, and me. I got to miss Science twice. Also we have a song, "Drill Ye Tarriers Drill." At the end it goes, "and drill, and blast, and FIRE!" You are supposed to yell out FIRE real loud because it's capitalized, but everyone is afraid to yell because if nobody else does then you look like an idiot. But Miss Allen is easy. One day I was in Music, a few days after the assembly with Officer Williams, and we were singing "Peace I Ask of Thee O River," and I was the only one who could sing the harmony part. So Miss Allen

---

13 **glee:** Kurzform von *glee club* (AE): Chor.
14 **billy goat:** Geißbock.
    gruff: schroff, barsch, ärgerlich.
17 **Drill Ye Tarriers:** amerikanischer *worksong* aus der Mitte des 19. Jh.s (*ye* [arch.]: *you*; *tarrier:* Streckenarbeiter).
20 **capitalized:** in Großbuchstaben.
24 **thee** (arch.): *you.*
25 **harmony part:** zweite Stimme.

made me stand up and sing it alone. Harold Lund
laughed at me and called me a sissy and I was embarrassed. Then somebody walked into Music. It was
Jessica, with a note from Miss Verdon the Art teacher.
5 Miss Allen told me to keep singing while she read the
note. Then I did something. I started to sing "Heartbreak Hotel." It is cool, man, it is Elvis, I can imitate
him perfect. I sang it louder and louder and closed my
eyes. When I opened them Jessica wasn't even looking
10 at me, and I stopped. But when she left she looked at
me and smiled like.)

I remembered this when I was looking out the
window in the Playroom, and then the person who
sang said something.

15 "Would you care for some bubble gum?"

It was the red-haired man. I didn't say an answer.

He sang again. "I'll walk alone, because to tell you
the truth."

The cars passed outside the window and I thought I
20 saw our car and I started to bang on the window but it
wasn't.

"I'll be lonely."

I watched it go, and I thought, Maybe it is our car
but my parents don't want me anymore because of
25 what I did to Jessica.

"I said, would you care for some bubble gum?" said
the red-haired man.

"No," I said. And then I didn't hear any more singing. I didn't turn around though. But I heard him blow
30 a bubble and it popped and he said shit.

6f. **Heartbreak Hotel:** Titel eines Songs von Elvis Presley.
20 **to bang:** hämmern, laut schlagen.

"You aren't supposed to swear," I said. "It's not good manners."

"You aren't supposed to chew bubble gum either," he said. "Except without it how would I ever get any cavities?"

"It gives you cavities."

"That's what I said."

I turned around. He was sitting in a little kid's chair.

"But you're not supposed to get cavities," I said.

"Says who."

"You aren't." I got real mad and turned back around to the window.

Then the man whispered, "I know, I know."

I sat down in the little orange chair by the window, and kicked some kicks in the rug, which sometimes gives you electricity.

"I like getting cavities," said the red-haired man. "I want to get all my teeth filled as soon as possible before it's too late. My dentist won't be around much longer. He'll be killing himself fairly soon now."

"Why?"

"Why what?"

"Why is he going to kill himself?"

"Oh," said the red-haired man, and popped another bubble. "Because he's a dentist. Wouldn't you?"

"What do you mean?"

"Well, everybody hates the dentist. Even dentists' sons. This guy's son hates him, but for another reason. See, when he was little, the dentist decided that he would pretend he wasn't a dentist, so his son wouldn't

---

19 **to be around:** da sein.

hate him. He told his son that he was a professional baseball player. He went and had a Tigers uniform made up, and every day he wore it out the door and wore it when he came home, only then he'd stop on
5 the way home and get it dirty. He had phony news-paper articles written up about him and slipped them into the Sports Section. But when the kid started school, it seemed that no one ever heard of his dad, so the dentist had all these phony baseball cards printed
10 up and brought them to the stores and slipped them into the bubble gum packs.

Finally he made friends with Ozzie Virgil, the Tigers' third baseman, took him and his wife out to dinner, did his kids' teeth for free. He got Ozzie to play along with
15 the scheme. So when the kid was eight years old, the dentist finally took him to a game. The kid was very excited. They went right to the dugout, but unfortu-nately they were too early and Ozzie Virgil hadn't showed up yet, so they wouldn't let him in and then
20 they ran into Ozzie on the way out and the first thing Ozzie said was, 'Hey, Stan, Joey broke a filling, could Gladys bring him by later today?'

That was five years ago. The dentist's son hasn't spoken to him since. It's only a matter of time before
25 he kills himself."

I walked across the Playroom to the toychest. There

---

2 **Tigers:** Name des Baseballteams von Detroit.
13 **third baseman:** (Baseball-)Spieler am dritten Base, am dritten Mal.
14 **for free:** gratis, kostenlos, umsonst.
14f. **to play along with the scheme:** das (abgekartete) Spiel mitspielen.
17 **dugout:** Trainerbank.
21 **Joey broke a filling:** Joey ist eine Plombe ausgebrochen.

was a doll in it, a girl who had brown hair with ribbons in it like Jessica. She didn't have any clothes on and I got a stomach ache. Also I was afraid of going to the dentist.

5 "I have to go today," I said to the red-haired man.

He nodded with his eyes closed, like he already knew. "By the way, Burt, my name's Rudyard."

There was another doll in the toychest, it was blond with no ribbons. I threw it at the wall and the arms fell
10 off. My stomach hurt so bad I could hardly stand up. It was like freezing inside my tushy, up inside me. And I had to go to the lavatory.

I was starting to have tears in my eyes, I bit my lip. I looked at the red-haired man, at Rudyard, and he
15 looked at me with his eyes. He got up and walked over to me and took out a handkerchief and wiped my eyes very soft.

"Dusty in here," he said. "Allergic to the dust in here."

20 I started to cry and he put his hand on my head.

"Rudyard, I have to go to the lavatory, there is something wrong inside my tushy. I'm afraid. I'm afraid of the dentist."

He did this to the back of my hair, he squeezed me a
25 little on my head and put me against him and he smelled like my dad.

"Rudyard, I have to go to the lavatory only I have never been down here, I don't know where one is here."

30 "I do," he said. "It's a good one too."

---

11 **tushy** (coll.): hier: Bauch.
18 (*to be*) **allergic to s.th.:** gegen etwas allergisch sein.

I was crying.

"Rudyard, something is wrong inside me. I am different than everybody else."

Rudyard squeezed my head and did this to my hair
5 and I pushed it against him.

"Me too, Burt. Let's go."

Today I got a letter. I thought it was from Jessica,
but it wasn't.

December 7

10 Dear Burt,
I just got off the phone with Dr Nevele and he told me
that it would still be a little while before the first visiting
day at CTRC, so I decided to sit down and write a little
note instead, while I'm still thinking about you.
15   How is everything, Sweetheart? Both your father and I
(and Jeffrey!) miss you very much and can't wait for you
to come home. We know that you are anxious to come
home too and that's one of the reasons I am writing this
little letter.
20   Dr Nevele sure sounds like a terrific guy to Dad and
me, Burt, and we think it would really be a shame if after
all the hard work and time he's put into helping you, you
didn't decide to help him too. It's only fair, Burt. He
really does want to help you. He knows a whole lot about
25 little boys and what makes them do the things they do,
and it would be a shame to waste his time, don't you
agree? We're sure you do. We all know that you are truly
sorry for what you did and want to make everything right

13 **CTRC:** Abk. für *Children's Trust Residence Center.*

69

as soon as you can, and so you will decide to help Dr Nevele real soon to find out what's wrong inside you and then you can fix it right away and come home. Won't that be terrific? We're sure it will be, and we know you want to do everything in your power to make it happen.

You know, Son, you're not the only one who needs help finding out why you did that horrible thing to Jessica. Your father and I are going to see a doctor too. Someone that Dr Nevele recommended, to ask him if he thinks it's something Dad and I might have done, some way we failed as parents. It turns out that Dad knows this doctor from the club, so we're all going to have lunch some time next week and talk about it. Won't that be nice? We're sure it will.

Jessica's mother came to see us the other night again. She's still very upset. We asked her to stay to dinner but she wouldn't. Guess she is still very angry about everything. Jessica is out of the hospital now. She mentioned writing you a letter, but her mother told her she couldn't, so please don't be disappointed if you don't hear from her. We're sure you understand, you're just such a terrific young man. Actually, your father and I don't think it's such a good idea for you to see her again, either. Her mother is enrolling her in a private school as soon as the new term starts, and we think maybe that's all for the best. We're sure you understand because you're such a smart little boy.

Oh, by the way! Kenneth came over this morning and he brought you some baseball cards that he said you have been wanting. How about those Tigers! We don't know if you can watch the games there at CTRC, but they sure are going great guns this season! Last week Dad took Jeff to a game and they had a terrific time! It was the best

24 **to enroll** (AE): anmelden.
32 **to go great guns** (coll.): Vollgas geben, groß herauskommen.

time they ever had! They're going to go again next week, and this time they're going to sit in Uncle Paul's box seats. Isn't that great? Too bad you can't be there. Some other time.

Dr. Nevele said it wouldn't be such a good idea to send the baseball cards now, so we'll keep them for you for when you get home. There's no one to trade them with there, so they'll be waiting for you right here at home. Also, there may be a few other presents waiting too! Remember that dinosaur you wanted at Maxwell's? Dad and I agreed to get it for you! So if you be good and help Dr Nevele it'll be waiting for you too when you get home.

Well, that's about all the news from here. Please think about helping Dr Nevele so you can come home and get your toys. Won't that be terrific? Sure it will!

Love,
Mom and Dad

2 f. **box seats:** vordere Sitzplätze im Stadion.
7 **to trade s.th. with s.o.:** etwas mit jdm. tauschen.

9

For the new semester at school I had Miss Iris for
Homeroom. She is nice as a teacher, she is young and
she wears lots of make-up. She has blond hair. She has
5 nail polish and nice clothes like on tv. She wears perfume which is divine. Also she is easy, man, she never
yells. Once she said to us, "I let you children walk all
over me," but I never walked on her.

(Last semester I had Krepnik, who is mean. One
10 time Andy Debbs picked his nose during belltime and
Krepnik saw. She screamed, "You disgusting child,
don't you realize that is the foulest habit?" But Andy
didn't say an answer because he is shy, and she yelled,
"Go to the lavatory and wash your hands!" Andy
15 leaned on his desk and then Krepnik said he'd have to
wash the desk now. "Who taught you such manners?"
screamed Krepnik, and Andy Debbs said, "Nobody, I
learned all by myself." Andy Debbs is from the Home.
Miss Krepnik is mean to Home kids because they are
20 poor, but I feel she is the foulest habit.)

But Miss Iris is nice to everyone. But one time
something happened. I came home and Miss Iris was

---

5 f. **perfume:** Parfüm.
6 **divine:** göttlich, himmlisch.
7 f. **I let you walk all over me** (coll.): ich lasse mir von euch auf der
Nase herumtanzen.
10 **belltime:** Zeit nach dem Läuten für Stillarbeit.
11 **disgusting:** abscheulich, ekelhaft.

in our kitchen eating lunch with my mom. My mom said, "Dolores just dropped by after the PTA meeting, would you like to join us, Burt?" I ran up to my room and slammed the door. It isn't right when you see teachers outside of school. Miss Iris was wearing slacks.

But the third day of the new semester Miss Iris announced that the next day we were going to go to the zoo for a trip. She passed out permission slips, they were mimeographed. I smelled mine for an hour. She said we were going to have a picnic at the zoo but everybody had to bring lunch.

The next day I woke up early by myself. I made myself breakfast, ketchup and a Mars bar. Shrubs came to call for me, he rang the doorbell and woke everybody up. All the classes in the third grade got to go to the zoo, Miss Hellman's room and Miss Craig's room and our room. We had a bus. Miss Iris counted everybody, then she came up to me and said, "May I sit next to you, Burt?" I said no, but she did anyway. Then we went.

Mimeograph. MIMEOGRAPH. Mimeograph.

At the zoo we had to have a buddy who was the person you sat next to on the bus, so Miss Iris was my buddy. I said, "Can't I have Shrubs?" and she said, "Why Burt, that hurts my feelings."

---

2 **PTA:** Abk. für *parent-teacher assembly:* Elternpflegschaft.
4 **to slam the door:** die Tür zuschlagen.
9 **permission slip:** Berechtigungsschein.
10 **to mimeograph:** hektografieren.
23 **buddy** (coll.): Kumpel.

At the zoo is trees and fences and cement things that have the animals in them, and refreshment stands. There is a trail that is big yellow elephant footprints. I asked Miss Iris if they are real and she said why of
5 course. We followed them. They went to the Zoo Train. I said, "Is the train so small because the elephant squashed it?" and she said, "Oh Burt, you're so precious," and she put the key that's shaped like an elephant into the Talking Storybook that tells about
10 the animals, and Shrubs said, "I'm going to push 'Hound Dog,'" but then the train came.

It is like the ones at Kiddyland, only realer. Miss Iris said, "Will you protect me from all the wild animals, Burt?" I said no.
15 The train went all around the zoo. Miss Craig told us to wave at all the animals and Marty Polaski said he would drop them a postcard. Sometimes the train turned a corner and Miss Iris slid against me and it made me feel funny. She had perfume. Then suddenly
20 Marty Polaski started screaming, "I'm getting mangled by a gorilla, I'm getting mangled by a gorilla!" Everybody turned around. He pointed and said, "Here's the gorilla." It was Marcie Kane, she sat next to Jessica, they were buddies.
25 After the train we went to the chimps. They were

---

3 **trail:** Spur.
8 **precious** (coll.): goldig.
11 **Hound Dog:** Titel eines Songs von Elvis Presley.
12 **Kiddyland:** Vergnügungspark für Kinder.
realer: *more real.*
20 **to get mangled:** zerfleischt, zerfetzt werden.
25 **chimp:** Kurzform von *chimpanzee:* Schimpanse.

74

picking their noses like Andy Debbs and Shrubs
started to sing

> Everybody's doin it
> Doin it, doin it
5 Picking their nose
> And chewin it, chewin it

Miss Hellman made him stop. She doesn't like music.
   We went to the snakes who stuck their tongues out
and I got scared, and we went to the penguins who
10 wore tuxedos, and we went to the deer. Then it was
lunch. I had a tuna fish sandwich, it was warm and
mushy how I like it, and an apple and a Twinkie. My
mom had left it in the fridge for me. (The bag had a
paper clip. She must have ran out of staples.) Each
15 Homeroom got a table in the picnic area. Miss Iris had
a thing of lemonade she made herself. Miss Hellman
had a box with pop in it, she made the bus driver carry
it.
   I like to eat by myself so I can pretend. At the zoo I
20 pretended I was up in the tree eating my lunch that I
killed with a knife and that down below were humans
who were the enemy because they didn't have good

10 **tuxedo:** Frack.
11 **tuna fish:** Thunfisch.
12 **mushy:** weich und matschig.
   Twinkie: Produktname einer Limonade.
14 **paper clip:** Büroklammer.
   staple: Heftklammer.
17 **pop** (coll.): Limonade oder Mineralwasser mit Kohlensäure, Sprudel.
19 **to pretend:** hier: in eine Fantasierolle schlüpfen.

citizenship in the jungle. Then something happened. One of the humans saw me and came over to the tree. It was a white hunter.

"Want this?" he said. He held out a bottle of Nes-
5 bitt's orange pop and I hit it out of his hand and it spilled all over his green dress because he was Jessica.

She looked at the ground. The pop dripped off her finger. She still had her arm out.

"I just thought you might want it instead of lemon-
10 ade," she said.

I said, "Umgawa."

Then Marty Polaski started yelling, "Burton has a girlfriend, Burton has a girlfriend!"

"You better shut up," I said.

15 "Make me."

"Make me make you."

"I don't make monkeys," he said, so I socked him. I aimed at his stomach but I hit his face by accident and he fell down. Then he kicked me in the peenie, and
20 I couldn't stand up. Everything went around and around. Then I rolled under him and he fell on top of me and I socked him again and he got up but I chased him and caught him and threw him down, but he kicked me in the peenie again and I couldn't see. He
25 was on top of me.

The next thing I knew he was gone, and I was on the grass and Miss Iris leaned over me. I could smell her perfume. She kept asking if I was ok. I got up. I had to lean on someone. He was right there. Shrubs.

---

1 **jungle:** Dschungel.
6 **to spill:** auslaufen, kleckern.
17 **to make monkeys:** Affen nachmachen.

Then I saw a crowd of children over by the drinking fountain. They were looking at Marty Polaski, who was on the grass with a cut in his head. Shrubs said that Jessica Renton had hit him with the Nesbitt's bottle
5 when he was on top of me. I saw Miss Hellman was holding Jessica real tight and yelling at her. The water fountain had the water coming out of a lion's head. He was puking.

I sat down at the picnic table and Miss Iris sat down
10 next to me. She did this to my hair, and said "Are you ok, Honey? Is there anything I can do for you?" "Yeah," I said. "Don't call me Honey, ok?"

Soon it was time to look at animals again. Everybody switched buddies. I got Shrubs. He walked with a
15 limp. I said, "Why are you limping?" and he said, "A lion ate my knee."

We had to go to the birds. I hate them because they aren't wild animals and they smell. When we got there Shrubs and me didn't go in, we waited outside and
20 made a plan to ambush Marty Polaski when he came out and throw my shirt over his head and beat him up. Then Shrubs said that he didn't want to because he wanted to go see the mooses because he knew one of them. I said who. He said Bullwinkle.
25 I feel that sometimes Shrubs is a moron. Once I

1f. **drinking fountain:** Trinkbrunnen (in öffentlichen Gebäuden).
8 **to puke** (coll.): reihern, kotzen.
14f. **to walk with a limp:** hinken, humpeln.
20 **to ambush s.o.:** jdm. (in einem Hinterhalt) auflauern (*ambush:* Hinterhalt).
23 **mooses:** *moose:* Elch(e).
24 **Bullwinkle:** Elch in einer Zeichentrickserie mit dem Titel *Rocky and His friends,* die zum ersten Mal 1959 auf ABC gesendet wurde.

taught him idiot, and he stood on his front porch and
said idiot to everyone who walked past his house.

Everybody started to come out of the bird house.
The first one out was Miss Iris. She said, "Burt, why in
5 the world do you have your shirt off, do you want to
catch pneumonia on top of everything else?" I said yes.

Then Jessica came out and she saw me and walked
over to me, and I was embarrassed because you could
see I had a crewcut on my stomach.

10 "It doesn't matter that you don't have your shirt
on," Jessica said. "Germs and bacteria give you sick-
ness, not drafts. I'm just telling you."

"How do you know?" I said.

"I read it in a magazine."

15 "No you didn't, you're too young."

"I did," she said. "We get them in the mail at my
house. My daddy's a high school teacher and he lets
me read all I want."

"Big wow," I said, and I put my shirt back on, only I
20 buttoned it crooked and had to do it over. "Ig bay eal
day," I said. (This is Pig Latin. It is eat nay.) Then I saw
Shrubs was asking the man from the zoo where the
mooses were. Then we all went to look at the porcu-

---

1 **front porch:** Veranda an der Hausvorderseite.
6 **pneumonia:** Lungenentzündung.
9 **crewcut:** Bürstenhaarschnitt; hier: Gänsehaut.
11 **germ:** (Krankheits-)Keim.
   bacteria: Bakterien.
12 **drafts** (AE, pl.): Zugluft.
19 **big wow!** (coll.): haste Töne!, was du nicht sagst!
20 **crooked:** schräg, schief.
21 **Pig Latin:** etwa: Küchenlatein.
23f. **porcupine:** Stachelschwein.

78

pines. They were all sleeping in a hole, you could hardly see them. I remember once on "Popeye" a porcupine shot needles at him and then he drank some water and it came out all over him. Jessica leaned on
5 the chain around the porcupines. She was angry.

"You didn't have to knock the bottle out of my hand," she said. "You could have said, 'I don't care for any thank you.' It stained my dress."

"I was like Tarzan," I said.

10 "You're mental," she said, and went to the llamas.

In the same thing as the llamas there was a bird, he was large. It was a Kukaberra. Jessica looked at him, and I sang a song, I learned it in Music.

    Kukaberra sits
15   In the old gum tree
    Merry merry king
    Of the bush is he
    Laugh Kukaberra
    Laugh Kukaberra
20   Gay your life must be.

Jessica looked at me for a minute, she listened to my song. Then she like shook her head.

"It doesn't cost anything to be nice," she said. "My dad said so."

25 "So?"

"So what?"

"So?"

"So what?"

12 **Kukaberra:** australischer Häher.

The llamas were all sleeping but they weren't in holes, so you could see them.

"Sometimes I don't read magazines," said Jessica. "Sometimes I just look at the pictures. I like to look at
5 clothes. They are very elegant."

"I never look at clothes," I said. "Never."

"You look at Miss Iris' clothes," she said.

"Do not."

"Do so," said Jessica. "She sits next to you all the
10 time and you look at her clothes and when she crosses her legs you look at her shoes. I saw you on the bus."

Then we both looked at the llamas. I think they are spelled wrong.

"There's a pretty one," Jessica said. "He's all black
15 with white socks like my horse."

"You don't have a horse."

"Do so."

"Where?"

"That's for me to know and you to find out."
20 I looked at the llama. He spit on the ground.

"Once I had a horse, Jessica, and I told him to step on Miss Filmer's head and then blood shot out of her eyeballs and they took her to the furnace and burned her up and I rode away on my horse."
25 "I bet she smelled shitty," said Jessica, and I got angry.

"You aren't supposed to say shit," I said. "It's swearing."

But Jessica just walked away saying, "Shit, shit,
30 shit."

---

23 **furnace:** Schmelzofen.
25 **shitty** (vulg.): wie Scheiße.

Then we went to the bison. They were all sleeping. No holes.

"I can swear if I want to, it's a free country, Burton," said Jessica.

"My name isn't Burton," I said. "It's Randy." (I don't know why I said this.)

Then we went to the alligators who are my favorite animals because once I almost got one in Miami Beach Florida when we were there, they sold them in little cardboard boxes. Babies. At the zoo they were on an island that had a pit around it and then some grass and then a chain. No cage. I looked at them. (I have an alligator at home, his name is Allie. He is dead. I got him at the airport, he has stuffing.) They were all smiling. So I climbed over the chain and walked over the grass up to the side of the pit, and I leaned over and said, "Hi, alligators."

There were five of them. They were all sleeping and one of them had his mouth froze open. I decided to pet them while they were sleeping. That's when I heard the whole third grade screaming. I turned around and saw Miss Iris running back and forth back and forth. Shrubs said, "It's ok, Miss Iris. I think he knows them."

But Miss Iris screamed, "Come back here right now, Burton, or I'll brain you."

"His name isn't Burton, it's Randy," someone said. I turned around. Jessica was standing right beside me.

---

1 **bison** (pl. *bison*): Bison, nordamerikanischer Büffel.
11 **pit:** Grube, (Wasser-)Graben.
14 **he has stuffing** (coll.): er ist ausgestopft (*stuffing:* Füllung).
19 **froze open:** *frozen open:* offen stehend, weit geöffnet.

"You better get out of here," I said. "They'll kill you and eat you up, Jessica, they aren't your friends."

"I'll introduce myself," she said. The wind blew her dress a little, you could see her knee socks. And one of the alligators swished his tail.

"I'm Jessica Renton," she said to the alligator.

"They don't understand," I said.

"I think they're French alligators," she said. "Once I saw a cartoon where Popeye socked an alligator and he went up in the air and came down as suitcases."

"So what?"

"Nothing," she said. Then she started to walk up to the alligators. I grabbed her arm.

"Let go."

The children screamed louder. Miss Iris was biting her hand and waving at a man from the zoo.

"Jessica," I said.

"My name isn't Jessica."

"What is it?"

"Contessa. My daddy calls me that. But you can't."

She walked toward the alligators and one started to walk around.

"Je m'appelle Jessica," she said.

Suddenly somebody grabbed us. It was the man from the zoo. But Jessica pulled her arm away real fast and started running and when he looked at her I got away too. We jumped over the chain and ran away. We ran past the leopards. (Once I saw Popeye put spot

---

5 **to swish one's tail:** den Schwanz schnell hin und her bewegen.
20 **Contessa** (Ital.): Gräfin.
23 **je m'appelle** (Fr.): ich heiße.
28 f. **spot remover:** Fleckenmittel.

remover on one.) We ran past the bears who were sitting up like dogs. We ran past the seals. (They play horns on tv and are boring.) We ran past the giraffes and ran until we got to the elephants. Jessica beat me,
5 she is fast, man. She wasn't even out of breath.

And suddenly all the children from the third grade came running up to where we were, it was a stampede, they were all yelling. Miss Iris came too, she was running. I have never seen Miss Iris run before, it looked
10 wrong. Miss Hellman and Miss Craig came too. Hellman grabbed me on the arm and started to shake me. Then Jessica turned around.

"Miss Hellman, didn't you say we could all get ice cream when we got to the refreshment stand? It's right
15 there. Can we?"

All the children started singing "We want ice cream, we want ice cream!" and they pulled on Miss Hellman till she let go of me. "All right," she said.

They went. Everyone had ice cream except Jessica
20 and me. She was leaning on a sign, looking at the elephants. The sign said

DON'T MISS OUR
RIB-TICKLING ELEPHANT SHOW
AT 4PM and 5:30!

25 It was hot. I looked at the elephants, they made dust when they walked, there were three of them. They

---

2 **seal:** Seehund.
2f. **to play horns:** etwa: einen Ball auf der Schnauze balancieren (Seehund).
7 **stampede:** wildes Getümmel.
23 **rib-tickling:** zwerchfellerschütternd.

were all gray and dried up and cracked. They moved in
slow motion back and forth back and forth. Then two
of them moved backwards and the middle one turned
in a circle. Then they all went forwards, then they all
5 went backwards. It was so slow it seemed like weeks.

(I was going to give the call, and they would wake
up and carry me off to the jungle, but I didn't.)

Behind us the whole third grade was talking and eating ice cream and getting yelled at.

10 Jessica stood next to me. "Look at the elephants,
Randy," she said.

"My name isn't really Randy," I said.

"I know," she said.

And we stood there next to each other. The ele-
15 phants went back and forth back and forth.

Jessica said, "Look, Burt, they are doing their elephant show in their sleep. They're sleeping, but they
can't stop."

Miss Iris didn't sit next to me on the bus ride home.
20 She sat next to Marty Polaski.

---

1 **cracked:** hier: mit rissiger Haut.
2 **slow motion:** Zeitlupe.

10

On the way home from school after the zoo I got in a
fight with Harold Lund. He is a big grease who is
friends with Marty Polaski. He ambushed me, which is
dirty fighting, man, and jumped on me and pinned me
with his knees on my shoulders till Shrubs smashed
him in the head with a garbage can and we both ran
home.

When I got home the first thing my mom said was
"Don't open up your mouth," because my pants were
green on the knees from the grass. (They were new, I
got them at West's Clothing where they don't have
doors on the little rooms and a girl saw my underpants.) "It's a crime," said my mother. "Who beat you
up this time?"

"The Jehovah's Witnesses," I said.

"What?"

I walked away. She chased me and grabbed my arm.

"Tell me the truth, young man," she said.

So I told her. I got run over by a car which was
drove by a Jehovah's Witness and he got out and said I
wasn't a Jehovah's Witness but I said I was, only he
didn't believe me and then we had to arm wrestle and
I beat him because he was weak and then a negro

---

5 **dirty:** unfair.

13f. **underpants** (pl.): Unterhose.

16 **Jehovah's Witnesses:** Religionsgemeinschaft der Zeugen Jehovahs.

23 **to arm wrestle:** Armdrücken machen.

came and said I could be a negro if I wanted so I said ok and then the Jehovah's Witness got mad and pushed me on the grass and then I came home.

I walked upstairs to my room. My mom yelled, "You get back down here and tell me the truth." But I didn't.

(I don't know what Jehovah's Witnesses is. I think it's when you wear a sport jacket.)

I sat on my bed and picked up somebody. Monkey Cuddles, he was waiting for me. He said he saw out the window and it was me who beat up Harold Lund, not Shrubs. I threw my pants down the clothes chute, it is in Jeffrey's room behind the door. It is a little door like the milk chute only it goes down the basement for dirty clothes. I wish I could go down the clothes chute but I am too large. And my pants didn't go down. They got stuck halfway, you could hear. So I had to throw a book down it which is how you unplug the clothes chute. I went into my drawer to get *Learn to Spell, Book I*, which I kept in my dresser to study for the Spelling B.

Only it wasn't there. I lost it. (I am messy. I don't pick up after myself. My mom says, "I'm sick and tired of picking up after you, I'm going to stop and just let the garbage pile higher and higher until there isn't any more room, then what will you do?" And I said, "Move to Florida.") But instead of *Learn to Spell, Book I*, there was another book. *From Little Acorns.*

---

12 **clothes chute:** Kleiderschlucker, -rutsche, -klappe.
18 **to unplug:** hier: frei machen.
22 **messy** (coll.): schlampig.
23 **to pick up after o.s.:** sein Zeug, den eigenen Dreck wegräumen.

My mom left it in my room after she read it to us. I looked in it. It had many pictures. There was Grandma and Grandpa and a little boy and a little girl and pigs and baby pigs and cows and baby cows, and chickens
5 and eggs. And a peenie.

I closed it, it made me feel funny inside me. I sat down on my bed. Then the door opened up and a chicken walked in my room, it had a comb that was red. It was like skin and flopped from side to side. It climbed
10 up on my bed and started to walk toward me and I tried to push it away. Then there was another chicken and then another one. My room was full of them, and they were all laying eggs and making noise, and then the one on my bed started to peck at my peenie and I got scared
15 and hit it, and the comb on it started to swell up and get big and then I touched it with my finger and white stuff came out on my hand. Then it wasn't a chicken. It was Jessica. She sat on my bed and had her hand up her dress and was looking at me.

20 "Burton, are you all right in there?" my mom yelled from the stairway, "are you all right?"

I opened the door and rubbed my eyes.

"You've been sleeping," she said. "Well it's almost time for dinner. Wash your face and come down. And
25 don't mouth off to your father, he's in one of his moods."

I went in the bathroom and washed. (I used Sweetheart soap, it is my favorite, it has carving on it.) When

---

9 **to flop:** hin und her wackeln.
14 **to peck at s.th.:** an etwas herumpicken, auf etwas einhacken.
25 **to mouth off to s.o.:** vorlaut gegenüber, frech zu jdm. sein.
28 **carving:** eingeritztes oder erhabenes Muster, Motiv.

I went back into my room to change there wasn't any
chickens or Jessica. I put *From Little Acorns* back in
my dresser and went downstairs for dinner.

"I thought you were going to study for the Spelling
5 B," said Jeffrey. He was looking at girls in a magazine,
in the underwear ads.

"It's a free country," I said.

"Perch on this," he said and gave me the finger,
which is swearing. My dad hit him. He was in one of
10 his moods.

For dinner we had brisket. It was delicious and nutritious. Except Jeffrey kept horseplaying. He kicked
me under the table. But after dinner he helped me
study for the Spelling B.

15 The Spelling B was two weeks after the zoo. It was
Fall, October. (I remember because my dad gave me
his yellow windbreaker. It is cool, man, it has big
sleeves that are like puffy on me and it is plastic not
cloth, only the zipper is broke, that's how I got it.)
20 For two weeks Jeffrey helped me study. I used *Learn
to Spell*, books I, II, and III. Jeffrey had two from before, and Miss Iris gave me one. Also I used a dictionary. Jeffrey asked me words and I spelled them.

---

6 **ad:** Kurzform von *advertisement*.
8 **perch on this!** (vulg.): du kannst mich mal!
   to give s.o. the finger (vulg.): jdm. den Stinkefinger zeigen.
11 **brisket:** Bruststück vom Rind.
11 f. **nutritious:** nahrhaft.
12 **to horseplay:** Blödsinn machen.
17 **windbreaker:** Windjacke, Anorak.
18 **puffy:** weit, bauschig (Ärmel).
19 **broke:** *broken*.

First there is the class Spelling B and then the grade Spelling B and then the school Spelling B and then the city Spelling B, and then I don't know what Spelling B. I won my class one on numerous. I got a sticker on my forehead. It was a turkey. (Miss Iris was out of stars.) My mom said she was very proud of me and took me to Maxwell's after school and said I could pick out an inexpensive toy. I asked for Zorro. He is a model already put together. He is swift. There are lots of models at Maxwell's but Zorro is the biggest. Jeffrey said it's because he's from another company but I think he's Spanish. He was too expensive anyway, so I got a new bag of men. But Mom said if I won the grade Spelling B I could get Zorro.

The night before the grade Spelling B I was nervous. I had pleurodynia. So I took *Learn to Spell, Book I* into the bathroom with me and stayed there and tested myself.

"Burton, what are you doing in there?" my mom said.

"Nothing," I said.

"It sounds like you're singing 'Heartbreak Hotel,'" she said. (But it sounded exactly like the record. Exactly.)

Then next day I didn't even have nerves, which surprised me but I didn't. I got up and had breakfast and Shrubs called for me like always and then he went into

---

4 **sticker:** Aufkleber.
5 **Miss Iris was out of stars:** Fräulein Iris waren die Sterne ausgegangen, Fräulein Iris hatte keine Sterne mehr.
8 **inexpensive:** billig.
25 **to have nerves** (coll.): nervös sein.

the den and stole candy out of Mom's glass thing like always, and we went. I told him that maybe I would get Zorro from Maxwell's and he said, "Goll."

At belltime I had ants in my pants. (Not really ants.)
5 We had Ackles the Science teacher for belltime. She is from the South, she calls us "folks." And also she has a book that she gives you an E in when you're bad. She calls them "big fat E's." That morning Marty Polaski got up for Show and Tell. He said, "Yesterday I was at
10 home building an electric chair when I had an accident and cut off my finger. But I picked it up off the floor and put it in a little box so I wouldn't lose it. And here it is." He took out a little white box and inside was cotton and on the cotton was his finger. Miss Ackles
15 turned white like she was going to ralph. Marcie Kane layed down on the floor, she died. And then Marty showed us, there was a hole in the bottom of the box that he stuck his finger through. (He got a big fat E from Miss Ackles.)
20 Then a girl came into the room and said, "Would the finalists for the Grade Three Spelling B please come with me to room 215." And I went.

In room 215 all the children stood against the wall like a firing squad. Miss Iris and Miss Krepnik sat in
25 the middle of the room on teacher's chairs. Miss Krep-

---

3 **goll:** *golly:* Ausruf der Überraschung.
4 **to have ants in one's pants** (coll.): kribblig (vor Nervosität) sein, Hummeln im Hintern haben (*ant:* Ameise).
7 **E:** (Note) Fünf.
9 **show and tell:** beliebtes Spiel in der Schule, zu dem die Kinder Gegenstände mitbringen, um ihren Mitschülern davon zu erzählen.
21 **finalist:** Endkampfteilnehmer.
24 **firing squad:** Erschießungskommando.

nik took her mean pills, you could tell. I stood across from the window side of the room and looked out. It was Fall and the leaves were falling off the trees. They went bald.

5 Room 215 is Miss Iris' room. It still had the bulletin board in it that I made for Open House. (Open House is when you come to school at night with your parents and stand in line to meet your teachers and hear them lie about you. The bulletin board was of a horse that
10 said "Gallopin' Good Grades!" and they put papers on it. I made it. I am an artist, I am good at drawing. Miss Verdon the Art teacher says I have talent. I like to make bulletin boards. You get to use teachers' scissors which are pointy and could put an eye out.)

15 When everyone was quiet Miss Iris told us the rules of the Spelling B.

"We will ask each student one word at a time. You may ask us to repeat it. You may ask us to use it in a sentence, but once you begin to spell we can't say any-
20 thing else and you can't change your mind once you've begun."

Then the door opened. It was Miss Lipincott. She is a teacher. She had someone with her. She was pulling her by the arm. It was Jessica.

25 "Now you just take your place with the others, young lady," Miss Lipincott said. "Hurry up."

Jessica gave Lipincott a dirty look. She had a book with her. It was black, from the library. "You'll have to put the book down, young lady," said Miss Krepnik.

---

1 **to take one's mean pills** (coll.): besonders gemein sein.
5f. **bulletin board:** Schwarzes Brett, Anschlagbrett.
6 **Open House:** Elternsprechtag.

"You can't have a book with you during the Spelling B."

"I had to practically drag her here," said Lipincott.

"Why?" asked Miss Iris.

Lipincott turned to Jessica and said, "Why?"

"How the hell should I know?" said Jessica. (It was nasty language. In front of teachers, everyone froze.)

"I'm not going to encourage that filthy mouth of yours by pursuing this further," said Lipincott. "Now you just put that book under a desk and we'll get on with this."

Jessica waited for a minute, but she put the book under a desk. Miss Krepnik said, "Thank you, Fran," to Miss Lipincott, who left.

Then the Spelling B started.

Miss Krepnik asked Mike Funt brat.

"Could you use it in a sentence please?" said Mike.

"Yes. He is a brat."

"Brat. B R A T. Brat."

Miss Iris asked Marion Parker roam.

"Could you use it in a sentence please?"

"Yes. I like to roam."

"Roam. R O A M. Roam."

Miss Krepnik asked Tommy Halsey bicycle.

"Bicycle. B Y –." But he knew he goofed. He almost started to cry and sat down.

Miss Krepnik asked Ruth Arnold bicycle.

"Could you use it in a sentence please?"

"Yes. I have a bicycle."

---

8 **filthy mouth:** Schandmaul.
16 **brat** (coll.): Balg, Gör, Früchtchen.
20 **to roam:** herumziehen, -streunen.

"Bicycle. B I C Y C L E. Bicycle." She spelled it smiling. I hate Ruth Arnold, she is always the teacher's pet because she is so smart and plays the violin. Once I asked her a riddle:

5   "Reading and writing and racing on Mars.
       Can you spell it without any r's?"

Ruth Arnold couldn't. So I told her, "I T. It. Ha ha." To be candid, I would like to kill Ruth Arnold. One time in Social Studies she told on me because I was showing
10 Shrubs how to make it look like you're pulling your thumb off. I got sent out in the hall and had to miss a test and then Crowley gave me an E on it, and I wasn't even talking. (It was pantomime. We learned it in Homeroom in a Unit entitled "Let's Put On a Play!")
15 Miss Iris asked me autumn. I spelled it easy, I didn't even ask for a sentence. But Ruth Arnold raised her hand and said, "Miss Iris, that isn't fair because it has the word autumn right on the bulletin board. It says on the papers, 'An Autumn Poem.' Burt made the bulletin
20 board, he saw."

"I did not, you lie!" I said.

"That was not a signal to talk," said Krepnik. But she said Ruth Arnold was right and Miss Iris had to ask me another word.
25 "Well just a minute, Helen," said Miss Iris. "I don't think it's fair that Burt should have to spell an extra word. Besides, he didn't put those papers up there, I did. He just put up the bulletin board."

---

9 **Social Studies:** etwa: Gemeinschaftskunde.
  to tell on s.o.: jdn. verpetzen.
13 **pantomime:** Pantomime, szenische Darstellung ohne Worte.

"Then I'll give the word," said Miss Krepnik.

"You will not," said Miss Iris. She was turning red and all the children stared.

"Look, it's on the board," said Krepnik.

5 "Are you crazy, he can't see the board from there."

The two teachers got real angry and looked daggers at each other. Then Miss Iris said that if anyone was going to ask me another word it would be her. So she asked me alternate.

10 "Could you use it in a sentence, please?" I said.

"Yes. The teachers who give the words at a Spelling B are supposed to alternate."

"Alternate. A L T E R N A T E. Alternate."

Then Miss Krepnik asked Joan Overbeck destroy.
15 And Miss Iris asked Irving Klein neglect. And Miss Krepnik asked William Gage wholesome, but he got it wrong, only he wouldn't sit down. Miss Krepnik said to sit down but William wouldn't, he just stared at the floor. He didn't want to be out. So Miss Iris said, "Wil-
20 liam, Honey, listen. These are the rules and we've got to obey them. There will be other chances for you next semester. I bet your parents will be very very proud of you when they hear how far you got." Then William sat down and Miss Krepnik looked daggers at Miss Iris
25 again.

Then it was Jessica's turn. Miss Iris asked her receive but Jessica looked like she didn't hear.

"Jessica."

"What?"

---

6 **to look daggers at s.o.** (fig.): jdn. mit Blicken erdolchen.

9 **to alternate:** (ab)wechseln.

16 **wholesome:** gesund.

"Receive."

"Receive what?" said Jessica. Everybody laughed. Krepnik got real mad. "Receive is your word, young lady. Spell it please."

5 "I T."

"Jessica, maybe you would prefer to go straight to the office and forfeit your right to be in this Spelling B," said Krepnik. "Is that what you want? Do you think your parents would find that amusing?"

10 Miss Iris said, "Jessica, either spell the word or you may take an E in spelling for the whole semester. Is that clear?" She was mad too.

But I thought something. That Jessica is very smart in school and that she would win the Spelling B, and 15 not me. I got very nervous.

"Receive," said Miss Krepnik.

"Could you use it in a sentence, please?"

"Yes. I like to receive things."

"Receive," said Jessica. "M P X L Y H H O. Receive."

20 Nobody said anything, they just stared. Jessica just stood there. Then very quiet Miss Krepnik said, "Go to the office, young lady."

Jessica got her book out from under the desk and walked out the door.

25 Dave Sutton went "Dum de dum dum." (It is the music from "Dragnet," on tv.) "That was not a signal to talk," said Krepnik.

Then the words got hard. The students couldn't spell

---

7 **office:** hier: Rektorat.

to forfeit a right: ein Recht verwirken, verlieren.

26 **Dragnet:** wörtl.: Schleppnetz; Name einer amerikanischen Fernsehserie (1967–70).

them and they went down. Helen Tressler went down
on cellophane. So did Audrey Burnstein, who has
braces, and five students went down on yacht until
Ruth Arnold spelled it. She also got nausea and in-
5 criminate. I spelled decorum and hospitable. Then
there were only four of us left. Nancy Kelton went
down on fertilizer and so did Sidney Weiss. But Ruth
Arnold got it. Then it was just her and me.

Miss Iris asked me gratitude.

10 "Could you use it in a sentence, please?"

"Yes. I have a lot of gratitude."

"Gratitude. G R A T A T U D E. Gratitude."

"Ruth Arnold," said Miss Iris. "Gratitude." And I
knew I spelled it wrong. Suddenly I felt like I was
15 going to fall down. I had lost the Spelling B.

Ruth Arnold said, "Gratitude. G R A T T I T U D E.
Gratitude." She spelled it wrong too. I almost laughed.

Miss Krepnik asked me aisle.

"Aisle. A I S L E. Aisle." I guessed but I was right.
20 Then Miss Iris asked Ruth Arnold conniption.

"Conniption. C O N I P T I O N. Conniption," said
Ruth Arnold.

But I knew it. I knew it because my mom says that I
have them, so one day I looked it up in the dictionary

---

1 **to go down** (fig.): ausscheiden, unterliegen.
3 **braces** (pl.): Zahnspange.
  yacht: Jacht.
4 **nausea:** Übelkeit.
4f. **to incriminate:** (eines Verbrechens) beschuldigen.
5 **decorum:** Anstand.
  hospitable: gastfreundlich.
9 **gratitude:** Dankbarkeit.

and I knew how to spell it. I spelled it. Then Miss
Krepnik asked me necessary.

"Necessary. NECESSARY. Necessary."

Miss Iris started clapping. Krepnik looked at her,
but I had won the Spelling B for the whole third grade
and I started clapping too. I clapped for me. Miss
Krepnik said it wasn't called for but I clapped and
clapped. I clapped until all the other children were
gone. Miss Iris kissed me on the forehead and said,
"Why don't you go down to the office and collect your
prize. Here's a pass."

I did.

Outside the office somebody was sitting on the
bench in the hall where the bad kids sit when they wait
to get yelled at by the principal. It was Jessica. I went
past her, into the office, I didn't say anything to her because she didn't see me because she was reading her
book. I asked the secretary with red hair about my
prize. It was a dictionary. She said to wait outside on
the bench. So I did. Jessica was still reading. I saw the
book, it was *The Black Stallion's Sulky Colt*.

The bell rang for classes to pass. Everyone went in
their lockers. They saw me sitting on the bench. I said,
"I'm not bad, I just won the Spelling B," so they
wouldn't think I was bad. But Jessica didn't say anything, she just read. After a while she put the book
down and looked out in the hall, but not at anybody.

---

11 **pass:** hier: Eintrittserlaubnis.
21 **stallion:** Hengst.
    sulky: eingeschnappt, schmollend.
    colt: Fohlen.

At nobody. And she said, "By now I bet he's in Wyoming. He started in Montana with the whole herd, he is the leader because he is the biggest and the wildest, no one can ride him except me. But now he is coming
5 alone."

"Who's coming?" I said.

She turned around and looked at me on my face, and I saw her eyes. They are giants, man, green with brown pieces inside.

10 "Blacky," she said. "My horse."

I said, "Oh."

Then we didn't say anything for a long time. The classes stopped passing and the lockers stopped slamming and then it was quiet in the hall at school.

15 Then Jessica said something.

"You know, I let you win the Spelling B, Burt," she said. "Because you wanted to."

---

8 **giant:** Riese; riesig (groß); super.

11

Once I was five. I rode in the car frequent. I sat next to
Daddy in the front seat on the hump. The hump went
down the front seat where there wasn't any sewing. It
raised me up so I could see. It was my special place.
Once we drove all the way to Frankfort, Michigan, and
I sat on the hump all the way.

Then one day my dad took Jeffrey and me to Hanley-Dawson Chevrolet to buy a new car. We went in
our old car. I sat on the hump. Then we got in the new
car. It smelled funny. Daddy got in and started it. Then
we went. I looked out the back window and waved to
our old car. I said, "What about our old car, Dad?"
And he said, "That hunk of tin, who cares?"

I looked in the front seat. There wasn't any hump.
My dad said, "That's because this baby has the engine
in the back, see all the extra room it gives us?"

I put my chin on the back of the back seat and
watched our old car out the back window. I cried
maybe. Jeffrey said, "What are you crying about now,
baby?" And I said, "I don't have anywhere to sit."

---

3 **hump:** Buckel; gemeint ist die Erhöhung zwischen den Vordersitzen
 eines Autos.
4 **sewing:** hier: Stoffüberzug.
14 **hunk of tin** (coll.): Schrotthaufen, Rostlaube.

12

I have been at The Children's Trust Residence Center
for two and a half weeks now. Every day the mailman
comes but I don't get any letters from Jessica. And
5 every day I ask Dr Nevele if any letters come for me
and he says no.

This morning I was sitting at the table in our wing
where we have games sometimes. I was making Mr Potato Head. He is plastic, not a real potato like at home.
10 I was putting a nose in him when Mrs Cochrane came
in and said she had an announcement to make.

"I have very good news this morning," she said smiling very phony baloney. "The new swimming pool is
finished. As of today, all the children here at CTRC
15 may begin using it, when their turn comes. They have
made up a schedule, and would you believe it? We are
the very first group. Right after breakfast we can go
swimming."

All the children shouted "Oh boy!"

20 Except one. Me. I sat and made my Mr Potato Head.
I put another nose on him, a big one like Dr Nevele's
only it didn't have hair inside it like his, which makes
me sick, to be candid.

The first day at The Children's Trust Residence
25 Center they told me about the new pool they were
building and sometimes I could hear them, it is way in

---

14 **as of today:** ab heute.

the basement. Before, they used to take the children to the YMCA in a bus for swimming. But they stopped before I got here and I am glad because I hate the YMCA, I would like to kill it. (Once Shrubs' uncle
5 paid for me and Shrubs to join the YMCA for a year. He is goy. So is Shrubs' mom. I only went to the YMCA once because it scared me, there were crosses all over the walls and pictures of Jesus Christ and I saw in the shower part all the men had penises with long
10 sleeves.)

"Of course we must all be on our very best behavior," said Mrs Cochrane. "If we want to keep our swimming privileges. We can't let behavior problems go swimming, can we? It wouldn't be fair to the rest of
15 the children."

I put another nose on Mr Potato Head.

Manny said that he didn't want to go swimming because he didn't have a suit, and Mrs Cochrane said that bathing attire would be provided. That means
20 suits. All the children shouted Hooray! except Howie, who was picking his nose. I saw him. (I like to pick my nose sometimes because I like boogers. I fling them. At school sometimes I sit next to Marty Polaski and he picks his nose and then he shows it to me and says,
25 "This is a 1956 Chevrolet booger." Then he picks it again and says, "This is a 1954 Oldsmobile booger." He is good at funny jokes but he is a behavior problem.)

---

2 **YMCA:** Abk. für *Young Men's Christian Association:* CVJM.
 6 **goy:** Nichtjude.
19 **bathing attire:** Badekleidung.
22 **boogers** (coll., pl.): Popel.
   to fling: (weg)schnipsen.

By then all the children in our wing were jumping up and down singing, "We're going swimming! We're going swimming!"

Except me. Then Mrs Cochrane saw and she walked over to me and looked at Mr Potato Head. He was all noses.

When everyone was dressed we went to breakfast which was eggs with eyeballs in them, sunnyside up. I sat next to Robert. He cries all the time. So I said, "Hey, Robert, watch this. Let's say this egg is your eyeball, ok?" He said ok, and I stuck my knife in it and the yolk started running all over the plate. And he started crying. So I socked him in the mouth and his cereal sprayed all over Mrs Cochrane. She got real mad and grabbed my hand across the table, which was a fist, but I pulled it away and smashed it onto my plate and it broke and part of it hit Robert in the face and he started screaming. Everyone in the dining room turned to look. So I stood up on my chair and started walking on the table and stepped in everybody's plate and tipped over the water. I kicked my glass of orange juice and it went all the way across the room and hit Rudyard in the back, he turned around and saw me but he didn't say anything.

Mrs Cochrane got up and grabbed me around the waist and yelled for an attendant at the next table to help her and he got up and came and picked me up and I kicked him in the stomach so he grabbed my arms and wrapped them around me so I couldn't move

---

8 **eggs sunnyside up:** Spiegeleier.

12 **yolk:** Eigelb.

14 **to spray:** spritzen.

and pulled them real hard. He carried me out of the dining hall. Mrs Cochrane came too.

When we got to Dr Nevele's office there was someone else in there, the door was closed, so the attendant
5 sat me down on the bench and held me. Mrs Cochrane knocked on his door and went inside. I tried to bite the attendant but he pulled my arms real hard and it felt like he was breaking them. I couldn't move. Then Mrs Cochrane came out of the office and her face was red.
10 Right behind her was a woman. I stopped trying to bite the attendant. I just stared at her and she stared at me. I didn't know what to do. It was Jessica's mother.

She looked at me like she was frozen, like I was a monster. Then she looked away and didn't say any
15 words and I saw she was shaking.

Dr Nevele came out, he put his hand on her back and she looked at him and looked at me and then he nodded and she left the office. I didn't do anything. The attendant let go of me and Dr Nevele said to come
20 into his office.

"All right," he said. "What is it this time?"

"Nothing."

He took a stack of papers out of his drawer, but they slipped out of his hands and went on the floor.
25 "Shit," he said.

"You aren't supposed to swear, Dr Nevele," I said. He picked up the papers one at a time, but a couple clipped together were still there, under the desk. He didn't see them, but I did. I touched them with my
30 shoe.

---

23 **stack:** Stapel.

"All right," he said. "Who started it this time?"

"Me," I said.

"What happened?"

"Nothing. Can I go to the Quiet Room?"

5 "No, Burt," he said. "you can't. Every time you get a little upset you run off to the Quiet Room to write on that damn wall instead of talking to me. I want you to talk to me, Burt. Please."

"Dr Nevele," I said. "I will never talk to you," and I
10 stood up and went to his bookcase and put my hand on it like I was going to tip it over again. But he pushed me back in the chair and got out the seatbelt. He put it around me himself this time and pulled it tight. I tried to loosen it, it was pinching me.

15 "Just you sit there, Buster," he said. "And think things over for a while." And he walked out of the office. And I was alone.

I thought about once I was in Frankfort, Michigan, with my family and we went to Crystal Lake for swim-
20 ming only I didn't want to because I didn't know how, but they took me anyway. My dad put a life preserver on me that was cold and wet because somebody used it before, it was orange with buckles that pinched my tummy when he put it on. I cried and cried. He picked
25 me up and said, "Stop that, Son. Do you want everyone to know you can't swim?" And he made me ashamed. My father carried me into the water. He took me all the way out to the deep part, it was over my head. I screamed, "Don't drop me, please don't drop me," and

---

15 **buster** (coll.): etwa: Rambo, Rowdy.
21 **life preserver:** Schwimmweste.
24 **tummy:** Bauch.

he said, "I'm not going to drop you." "Take me back, please," I screamed. "Please!" But he wouldn't, he just carried me out further. Then he started to put me in the water. "No!" I screamed, but he started to let go of me.
5 He said, "What are you worried about, you have a life preserver on." And he put me in. I tried to hold on to him, I grabbed at him. "Hey, watch your fingernails," he said. "Don't, Daddy!" I yelled. "Don't, I will drowned!" But he did. He let go of me and suddenly I
10 couldn't see, it went over my head and I started sinking and it was freezing cold inside my ears and everything was dark and I couldn't hear. I tried to breathe but only water came inside and I started to choke. Then he picked me up. I coughed and coughed. I hit him with
15 my fists and cried. I screamed so hard I couldn't hear anything else. "You're all right, Son," he said. "You're all right." But I wasn't. He took me back then, but I said something to myself. I will never go swimming again.
20 Dr Nevele came back into the room. I had took off the seatbelt. I did it myself. He didn't see.

"You know, Burt," he said. "We have the new pool all finished here. But if you continue to disrupt in this manner I will suspend your swimming privileges. You
25 won't be allowed to go swimming."

So I walked up to his desk and took all the papers and threw them in his face and ran over to the window and smashed it with my fists.

8f. **I will drowned:** *I will drown, I will be drowned, I will get drowned.*
13 **to choke:** würgen; ersticken.
20 **took:** *taken.*
23 **to disrupt:** (den Ablauf) stören.
24 **to suspend:** aufheben, sperren.

"I want to go home!" I screamed. "I want to go home, I want to go home!"

Dr Nevele grabbed me.

"That's it," he said. "All right, go to the damn Quiet
Room."

I reached under the desk and took the papers that
fell off. I quickly put them in my pocket and went to
the Quiet Room.

I sat in the corner and sharpened my pencil to write,
with my teeth, it makes my tongue black like "I Love
Lucy" when she does her teeth like they fell out.

The door opened. It was Rudyard, he looked at me
in the corner and put his finger against his mouth
which means shush. He came in and sat down on the
floor across from me, facing the wall.

"High Sign," he whispered, and put his hand under
his chin and wiggled his fingers.

I looked at him.

"High Sign," he said, and did it again. Then he like
breathed and said, "This is the High Sign, Burt," and
did it again. "Just so you'll know."

He leaned back against the wall and closed his eyes
and opened them. He looked over me, at the wall.

"Excellent penmanship," he said. "Very straight
lines too."

I jumped up and stood in front of the wall.

"No!" I yelled. "You aren't supposed to look at it,
Rudyard, it is private property."

"Not even a little look?"

---

14 **shush:** pst!
19 **high sign:** eine Art Erkennungszeichen.
24 **penmanship:** Schreibkunst.

"No!"

He turned around and faced the other way and said, "Ok, Burt. It's a deal."

"And don't write on it anymore either," I said. "It's only for me to write on, Dr Nevele said."

He turned back around.

"Write what? What do mean don't write on it?"

I pointed to the place where it wasn't my writing, where he had wrote *He wanted to see time fly.*

"I didn't write that," he said.

He was lying though, because he wrote it, I knew he did. Then I saw he had something on the back of his belt and I asked him what it was. He told me it was hot sauce that you put in the mouths of the crazy children when they bite to teach them not to bite. I have seen it at The Children's Trust Residence Center. It is like on a little sponge and it makes the children's mouths burn so they don't bite anymore. They scream. But I never saw Rudyard use it. I asked him why he doesn't use it.

"I don't like spicy food," he said.

Then he didn't say anything and neither did I. We both sat just, on the floor. Then he got up and started to leave.

"Where are you going?" I said.

"Nowhere," he said.

And he walked across the hall to a special room they have. It is the Play Therapy Room, they take children in it and doctors watch them play with items

---

3 **it's a deal** (coll.): abgemacht!

13f. **hot sauce:** Tabasco-, Chilisoße.

21 **spicy:** scharf gewürzt.

and write things down. I had never been in it though. I followed Rudyard.

He left the door open and I walked in. He sat down in a chair in the middle of the room and all around him was things to play with, only they didn't look right. There was a big doll house with wooden people inside, there was a Mommy and a Daddy and even a doggy. There was a box with other wooden people in, there was a doctor and a nurse and a policeman and a postman. Rudyard folded his hands in his lap and sat just. He didn't say anything.

I took the little wooden postman out of the box and put him on my knee and he told me that Jessica was going to write me letters real soon and that he would bring them to me so don't worry. "Ok," I said. "I'm not worried."

"I am," said Rudyard.

"I wasn't talking to you."

"Good," he said. "Because I wasn't talking to you."

"Who were you talking to?"

"Me," said Rudyard, and he put his fingers up to his eyes and wiggled them.

"Don't do that," I said, because it made me nervous, he acts like a spaz sometimes and I don't like it. But he didn't stop. He did it more. I put down the postman and walked over to him and grabbed his hands to make them stop wiggling. "Don't do that."

"Oh," he said. "Were you talking to me?"

I walked over to the doll house and picked up the Mommy. Then I put her down and picked up the little boy. He was me. He went into the bathroom. He had pleurodynia, because he didn't want to go swimming.

Then Rudyard said, "I think I need a favor, Burt."

"What?" I said. The little wooden boy left the bath-room and went into the den, only he couldn't watch television because he didn't take his bath before Pop-eye.

5 "I was wondering if you'd help me. I have to go swimming today and I'm a little afraid is all."

"You're a sissy," I said.

"Thanks," said Rudyard. "Actually I am scared of several things. Death and swimming. That's why I'm
10 here. I'm supposed to be in the pool now, dying."

"You are not," I said. He was lying, man. He is a grown up so he wasn't scared. He was lying.

"I am," he said.

I threw the little wooden boy at him and shouted,
15 "You are not, you are not! You lie, man! Sissies are afraid of swimming, only sissies arc!"

But Rudyard didn't say anything. He just got up and picked the little wooden boy off the floor and held him in his hand. He held him in both hands.

20 First you go into the locker room. The lockers are smaller than the ones at school, but they are louder when they get slammed, like guns in my head. All the children run around and scream and hit each other and it makes me very afraid. They give you a towel but it
25 isn't soft like at home, it scratches me. You have to un-dress in front of everybody. They give you a bathing suit, but it isn't yours, and they make you go to the showers which is a big room that is very hot and full of other children that you don't know and the spray is so

29 **spray:** Duschstrahl.

hard it stings when it hits you and the room smells like
naked people.

Then you have to cross the hall to get to the pool. It
is very cold in the hall and the floor is slippery. I fell.
5 Everybody laughed at me until Rudyard came and
picked me up and looked at them and they all stopped.
And he held my hand and we went into the pool part.

He put a thing on me, it looks like a football with
cloth over it. First he put one on himself, only it was
10 too small to go around, so he put two together and put
them on. It looked funny. I would have laughed if I
wasn't so afraid. But before he put one on me he took
the buckle and breathed on it and rubbed it in his
hands. "I hate it when they're cold," he said, and he
15 buckled me up. And it wasn't cold.

There were many other children in the pool. They
were jumping in and splashing and yelling very loud.
Rudyard looked at me and put his hand out. He held my
hand and we walked together into the shallow part. It
20 was very cold. I almost yelled, but Rudyard yelled first.
He yelled, "It's too cold!" and he wouldn't go in. "Rudyard," I said, "the other children will think you're a
baby." And he looked at me and said he didn't care what
anybody thought. Except me. And I said, "We could just
25 go in to where we can stand up." And we went.

We were standing in the shallow part and there were
children splashing all around. Rudyard yelled at them
and they stopped splashing. He yelled that he was
afraid of the water. He told them to go to another part
30 of the pool to splash, and they went. He didn't even

15 **to buckle s.o. up:** jdn. an-, festschnallen.

110

care if they thought he was a baby. And I was glad he made them go.

"What do you think?" he said to me, and pointed out into the pool. "Should we try?"

5 I was scared, only he was scared too.

"I'm too short," I said. "It's too deep for me."

"Well," said Rudyard. "If I carried you, you wouldn't be too short, and I wouldn't be so afraid because you'd be with me."

10 I looked at him. He put his hands around me very soft and then he lifted me up and held me tight.

"Squeeze me," he said, "so I won't be afraid." And I squeezed him very hard. We went out into the pool.

All the children screamed so loud that you couldn't 15 hear anything. And suddenly Rudyard started screaming too. He yelled, "I'm afraid, I'm afraid!" But no one could understand him but me, and then I did something. I said, "You don't have to be afraid, Rudyard, I am here." And he like hugged me. The water was up to 20 my stomach.

"Sometimes it helps me to scream," he said. "When I'm afraid. It doesn't matter if anyone hears or not. It helps me when I'm afraid." And he squeezed me. "Squeeze me a little tighter, Burt," he said. "That helps 25 me too." And I did. The water was up to my chest.

Somebody threw a ball, it landed right in Rudyard's face. He got real mad and yelled at the boy to get it away. The kid was scared of Rudyard. I never saw him mad before. "I get real mad when I'm afraid," he said. 30 "Everybody does. Sometimes they don't even know it. Next time you get mad, think about it. Maybe you're afraid of something, you know? Then you don't have to get mad."

He started bouncing. Walking on the bottom up and down up and down, and the water came up higher on me, only it was ok, because he squeezed me tight, I knew he wouldn't let me go. And the water was up to my chin.

Then Rudyard squeezed me even tighter.

"It's too tight," I said. "You're hurting me." And he let go a little. He still bounced up and down. The football thing on my back was in the water and I felt it, it held me up. "Let go a little more," I said.

"I don't know, Burt," said Rudyard.

"It's ok," I said. "Let go."

He held on to my hands, and kept one arm around me too.

"Kick your feet," he said. I did. And I went up against him. Then I stopped and I went backwards, he held my arm. Then I kicked again and I went toward him again. All by myself.

Rudyard started to laugh. "You're swimming," he said. "Are you trying to make me look stupid?"

But I kicked my feet. And he let go of me a little more, he only held my wrist.

"Paddle with your hand!" he said. "Like this!" And I did, and I went up to him even faster.

"Push me away again!" I said, and he did and then I kicked and paddled and went up to him again, real fast.

Then a ball came and hit me on the head and my head went under the water and I couldn't breathe, everything was black. I tried to breathe, and then I

---

1 **to bounce:** hüpfen.

could. Because I was all the way out of the water, on Rudyard's shoulder, and he held me up high so I could breathe.

He was real mad. He swore at the kid who threw the
5 ball. Then he put me against him and said, "Let's get out now."

"No," I said.

"No?"

"I can do it, Rudyard. I was swimming, man. I can
10 swim, man." And then he looked into my face, my face was right in front of his, and he smiled at me with his whole face. "That's right, man," he said. And he put me back in the water. And walked right next to me the whole time with his hand under me almost touching,
15 and didn't let anybody come near me or frighten me again, all the way to the end of the pool. I grabbed the side and turned around. Rudyard was way behind me. He gave me the High Sign. And I yelled, "High Sign," and did it. Because I beat him, man. I swam all by my-
20 self. I swam, man.

When I got back from swimming I found something in my pocket. It was the papers I picked up off the floor in Dr Nevele's office.

12/17

25 The patient remains noncommunicative and uncooperative. I cannot but judge the continued interference by Rudyard Walton to be

---

26 **uncooperative:** nicht zur Zusammenarbeit bereit.
27 **interference:** Einmischung.

a factor in the lack of progress in this
case. Though the review board this week ad-
vised him to "defer to the wishes of the
psychiatrist in charge, despite personal
5 judgment," he has nonetheless found reason
to see even more of the patient than before.

Today I received a memo from him. For sake
of record, I attach it here:

Dr Nevele:
10 I am writing you this note in a sincere
attempt at diplomacy, which is an endeavor quite foreign to my usual modus
operandi. (You've noticed?) But I feel
strongly enough about the situation to
15 put forth this effort, among others
which you've noticed.

I must say this: Sheriff, you have
the wrong man.

Burton   Rembrandt,   though   probably
20 guilty of some crime (let us continue to
use the ill-fitting term for sake of

---

3 **to defer to s.o's wishes:** sich jds. Wünschen beugen.
4 **psychiatrist:** Psychiater.
  in charge: (mit einem Fall) betraut, (für einen Fall) verantwortlich.
5 **nonetheless:** trotzdem.
7 **memo:** Erinnerungsschreiben.
7f. **for sake of record:** der Vollständigkeit halber.
11 **diplomacy:** diplomatisches Vorgehen.
11f. **endeavor:** Bemühung, Anstrengung.
12f. **modus operandi** (Lat.): Vorgehensweise.
14f. **to put forth:** (Anstrengung) machen.
21 **ill-fitting:** unpassend.

poetry) involving a young girl, is certainly not a criminal. I demand another jury. Namely me.

This child is no more a threat to society than Orphan Annie. (At least he has irises.) The psychoses you seem bent on finding in his young psyche are no more than signposts that give clear directions to a place you've obviously never been to: Yourselfville.

Burton's been double-crossed, and he's mad. Wouldn't you be? He doesn't know it in his mind (forest for the trees) but he feels it in his guts (literally, sometimes), and it was partially this double cross that led him to the incident with Jessica Renton, and that continues to lead him into tantrums and silences here where he doesn't belong and knows it.

He is a human being in kid's clothing. He has the organs and the feelings of his species, but none of the rights. And he is not alone. This country is stewing itself in the no-

5 **Orphan Annie:** Waisen aus einem Comic-Strip, den Harold Gray 1924 unter dem Titel *Little Orphan Annie* für die *Chicago Tribune* schuf.
6 **iris:** Iris (Auge).
   psychosis (pl. *psychoses*): Psychose, vorübergehende psychische Störung.
10 **Yourselfville:** etwa: das eigene Ich.
11 **to double-cross s.o.:** jdn. betrügen, hinter's Licht führen.
25 **to stew o.s.** (coll.): im eigenen Saft schmoren.

tion that you're not a person until
you reach voting and drinking age.
It's wrong.

You don't get it, Doctor (with all
due respect), and because you don't get
it, you can't give it. Let him go home.
He isn't crazy, he isn't even strange.
We have met the enemy, and he is us.

Sincerely,
Rudyard Walton

Mr Walton notwithstanding (it seems to
me that his method of therapy depends
more on wit than on knowledge — his
remarkable imitations of his autistic
patients, supposedly used to establish empathy between therapist and patient, are
really more vaudeville performances than
therapeutic sessions), Burton Rembrandt's
behavior will be approached strictly by
this therapist, and the aberrations there-
of will not be allowed to flourish here.
I have filed a formal complaint against
Mr Walton, which will be heard by the
Board of Directors next week, and which

4f. **with all due respect:** bei allem Respekt.
11 **notwithstanding:** trotz, ungeachtet.
13 **wit:** Einfallsreichtum, Schlagfertigkeit.
17 **vaudeville** (AE): komödiantisch.
19 **to approach s.th.:** mit etwas umgehen, etwas behandeln.
20 **aberration:** Verirrung, Auswuchs.
21 **to flourish:** gedeihen, blühen.
22 **to file a complaint:** Beschwerde einlegen.

will result, if there's any justice, in
his removal from the staff of the
Children's Trust Residence Center once and
for all.

In the past week, Burton has been the
recipient of postal correspondence from
the girl in question, Jessica Renton. I
have telephoned her mother and will meet
with her shortly to discuss this matter.
I told her on the phone that I still feel
the child (Burton) to be severely disturbed, and informed her of upcoming
neuro-pathological testing to be done on
him to determine the possible effects of
certain medication on his aberrant so-
ciopathic behavior. The correspondence,
however, will be withheld from the patient
until he is judged to be psychologically
stable enough to assimilate this kind of
stimulation. It is my further judgment
that he not be informed about said correspondence until that time. Particularly
interesting in the letter is her reference
to nightmares about the incident with the

---

6 **recipient:** Empfänger.
12 **upcoming:** bevorstehend.
15 **medication:** Verabreichung eines Medikaments.
 aberrant: abweichend, abartig.
17 **to withhold s.th. from s.o.:** jdm. etwas vorenthalten.
20 **stimulation:** Reiz.
21 **said:** besagt.
23 **reference:** Bezug; hier: Erwähnung.
24 **nightmare:** böser Traum.

patient. What she says about this matter is too sensitive to expose him to at this time.

I copied this on the wall. I can copy, man. But I
5 don't understand. It is too big words.

---

2 **sensitive:** heikel.

13

After the Spelling B it started to get cold. I was surprised, I am always surprised at seasons. This is because I am a child and everything takes longer to me. I
5 think it will be summer forever. But it never is. (We had seasons in Science. Miss Ackles said that the sun hits us crooked or something, only I didn't understand, so I got it wrong when she put it on the Science test. I got an X on my paper next to that answer. X means
10 wrong. C means right. Miss Ackles uses a checking pencil to check our papers. Checking pencils are my favorite as school supplies except for reinforcements, they are red on one side and blue on the other. They are reversible, like jackets. No zippers.)
15 Soon the weather got quite freezing outside and all the leaves fell down and I had to rake them, which I hate, to be candid. It is like shoveling with holes in it. Lucky for me we have a tree who is a baby so we don't have many leaves. (Our old one got cut down. He was
20 dead.)
About a week after the Spelling B, Miss Iris announced that we were going to have a Halloween

---

10f. **checking pencil:** Korrekturstift.
12 **school supply:** Schulbedarf.
reinforcements (pl.): Ringbuchlochverstärker.
14 **reversible:** umkehrbar, beidseitig verwendbar.
16 **to rake:** zusammenrechen.
17 **to shovel:** schaufeln.

party in Homeroom. Everybody had to wear costumes
(except the Home Kids, because they are poor and
can't afford them, only Marty Polaski said they could
come as poor children. Miss Iris laughed. "You mean
ragamuffins?" she said. But I don't understand. I think
it is when you put like bread on yourself.)

Everyone was supposed to bring refreshments to the
Halloween party. I signed up for cookies. My mom
makes them, they are very scrumptious.

I wear costumes all the time, not just for Halloween.
They are quite marvelous as clothing. My mom makes
them for me. (Except for Tom Corbett Space Cadet,
which is from a store, she bought it for Jeffrey two
years ago and he gave it to me because last year he
went as a fruit.)

But my best costume is Superman.

I asked for a Superman suit a long time ago but my
dad said no I had enough costumes. Then one day he
brought home a box from the store and said it was
a surprise for his number-two son (which is me). I
opened it and it was a Superman suit only when I put
it on I didn't like it because it was baggy and shiny, not
like the real Superman who has a real tight one so his
muscles show. (He puts his hands on his hips and the
bullets bounce off.) But my dad said I had to wear it
anyway since he bought it so I had a conniption fit and
threw books down the stairs and got sent to my room.
Later my mom came and said she would give the

---

5 **ragamuffin:** Gassenkind in zerlumpter Kleidung.
9 **scrumptious:** lecker.
22 **baggy:** weit geschnitten, lose, ausgebeult.
   shiny: glänzend.

Superman suit to poor children and make me a real one for the Halloween party. I said, "Make sure it's tight."

That same night Jeffrey gave me a present, it was his ID bracelet, because he got a new one for his birthday. It is swift, man.

The next morning Shrubs called for me for school, like every morning. Then while I eat breakfast he sneaks into the den and steals candy from my mom's glass thing. (We have all different kinds, there is even one kind that squirts when you suck on them, I call them hand grenades.)

On the way to school that morning I told Shrubs about the Superman suit and he said "Cool, man," and then I showed him the ID bracelet and he said "Cool, man" again. He said he was going to make his Halloween costume out of cardboard boxes from the furniture store across the street. I said what are you going to go as. He said a cardboard box.

"You aren't supposed to eat candy before school," I told him. (He was eating it.) "It gives you worms, my mom said."

"Does not," said Shrubs. "I have ate candy my whole life and I never had any. Worms don't like candy, they eat dirt."

At school everyone talked about their Halloween costumes. Marcie Kane said she was coming as the

---

5 **ID bracelet:** Armband mit eingraviertem Namen (*ID:* Kurzform von *identity*).
11 **to squirt:** spritzen.
12 **hand grenade:** Handgranate.
23 **ate:** *eaten.*

Tooth Fairy. She looks like a tooth, I feel. She should be a cavity for a living.

All during belltime I drew Superman suits on my dividers. I always draw things that I want. I draw them
5 over and over until I get them. Last year I drew Bengali. He is a tiger. I saw him on television. He is like
real. He roars. I asked for him for Hanukah but my
dad said he was too expensive and I would get bored
after two days. I said, "Pretty please with sugar on it,"
10 and he said, "We'll see." This means no. So I drew
Bengali. I drew him and drew him. I drew him on
newspapers and in the margins of *My Weekly Reader*.
Then I got him, the first night of Hanukah. It was Bengali, man, he was big. But he had wires. There were
15 two buttons, one to go and one for the roar. Only the
roar sounded like burping, not real like on tv, and also
I didn't see the wires on tv, and also his head was different than the rest of him, it was like plastic and the
rest was fur. I got bored with him in two days.
20 I drew Superman suits. Just the suit, not the head. I
put the muscles in though. I drew them in Miss Iris'
room where I sit by the window and look out and pretend that Tarzan is in the tree outside and I climb out
and we swing and I give the call and save the school
25 when it gets surrounded by colored negroes in grass
skirts.

I was looking out the window when I heard Miss Iris
yelling. She yelled at Pat Foder, who was talking to

---

1 **fairy:** Fee.
2 **for a living** (coll.): von Beruf.
3f. **dividers** (pl.): Stechzirkel.
16 **to burp:** rülpsen.

Francine Renaldo who sits behind her. Pat Foder is about four years older than everybody because she flunked eight times. She is a grease, she has hair that looks like an explosion only she wears short dresses
5 with stockings which make me feel funny under my stomach. She always talks to Francine Renaldo, who only flunked twice but is ugly. She has a big nose and a mustache. (But once I went to the office to give a note to the red-haired secretary for Miss Verdon and Fran-
10 cine was on the bad kid's bench and she talked to me and she was nice.)

Miss Iris called my name.

"Burt, please pack up all your materials and move to the second seat in the row by the bookcase. Miss Re-
15 naldo will move back one seat. Maybe with someone sitting between them, Miss Foder and Miss Renaldo won't feel they have to visit with each other so much and disrupt the rest of us who are trying to study."

Marty Polaski said, "Who's trying to study?" and
20 Miss Iris heard him and gave him daggers.

I moved.

Pat Foder wears perfume, I smelled it when I sat down, and she turned around and looked at me and blinked her eyes at me. It made me feel funny.
25 Then we had Reading. It was a story entitled "The Red Dog." It is quite interesting as a story. It is about like a red dog.

Francine Renaldo touched my shoulder.

"Pass this, ok?" she said. It was a note for Pat Foder.

---

3 **to flunk:** sitzen bleiben, durchfallen.
8 **mustache:** Schnurrbart.
24 **to blink one's eyes at s.o.:** jdm. zuzwinkern.

I passed it. You aren't supposed to but I didn't want to get in trouble for talking.

Then Pat Foder said, "Pass this back." But I said no. Then I got in trouble for talking. Then later she made 5 me pass it, and called me "Sweetie," and blinked at me again. The whole day I passed notes for Pat Foder and Francine Renaldo. One of them said

I think Bill Bastalini is sweat.

So I corrected the spelling with my checking pencil. 10 Then Pat Foder asked me about how to spell and I got in trouble for talking again. Then it was time for Lunch.

The children started lining up to pass. Pat Foder turned around and asked if she could see my ID brace- 15 let. I said no.

"Please, Sweetie?" she said.

"No," I said. "And stop getting me in trouble."

"I'll give it right back."

"No."

20 Then she started talking, and she said she wouldn't stop until I let her see it. I let her see it. She put it on her wrist.

"Why does it say Jeffrey on it?" she said.

"Give it back."

25 Then our row got called to line up. She got up and went to the door. I tried to grab my ID but she pulled it away. In line she started showing it to everyone and saying we were going steady, but that Bill Bastalini

---

8 **sweat:** *sweet.*
28 **to go steady** (coll.): miteinander gehen, fester Freund, feste Freundin sein.

124

didn't know and when he found out he was going to tune me.

I got real mad and ran over and started to grab her arm. Then Miss Iris saw.

5 "What's going on here?"

"Nothing."

"He gave me his ID to go steady, Miss Iris," said Pat Foder.

"Did not!" I yelled.

10 "I thought you were going steady with Jessica Renton," said Marty Polaski, "I seen you kissing her at the zoo."

And I socked him, and Miss Iris shouted, "That's enough!" and I got embarrassed and everybody went 15 to Lunch but we had to stay behind and Miss Iris sent me to the office.

I had to stay after school on the bad kid's bench. Shrubs was there too. He always has to stay after school because he gets in trouble all the time. (Once 20 he got in trouble for writing his own note when he was absent, he said he had lung cancer.) This time he was in trouble for eating candy in Miss Crowley's room. She told him it was bad manners to eat if you didn't have enough for everybody, so Shrubs opened his desk 25 and threw thirty pieces of candy in the air and yelled, "Happy New Year!"

"Are you going out for Devil's Night tonight?" Shrubs said.

(Devil's Night is the night before Halloween when 30 you go out and soap windows and ring doorbells. You

---

2 **to tune s.o.** (coll.): jdn. vermöbeln.

125

are supposed to be little goblins like. They are juvenile delinquents.)

"I don't know," I said.

Shrubs said, "Your mom gave my mom a book she is supposed to read to me. It's called *From Little Acorns*."

"It's about how babies are born," I told him.

Shrubs said he already knew. He said, "First Dad goes to the shopping center and buys a balloon. It is white. Then he brings it home and wraps it in aluminum foil so he can put it in the freezer for later. Then my mom gets in her pajamas and they go to bed. Then he takes out the balloon and shows it to her and she is so happy she has a baby."

After school we decided to rake leaves. We have a company, the Shru-Bu Company, we rake leaves. Also we make things. We make houses, they are cardboard boxes with doors cut in them, and once we even made one out of wood with plastic bags for the roof. We had dinner in it, potato chips. Also we made a newspaper, the Shru-Bu News. I wrote it myself on carbon paper. I made five of them. Miss Moss bought all five, she lives two houses from Shrubs. Then Jeffrey took over and made himself the boss and I was supposed to be the reporter so he told me to go out and get news, so I went down Lauder and got the *News* off everybody's front

---

1 **goblin:** Kobold.

1f. **juvenile delinquent:** Jugendstraftäter.

11 **foil:** Folie.

12 **pajamas** (pl.): Schlafanzug.

16 **the Shru-Bu-Company:** Firma Shru-Bu (aus den Anfangsbuchstaben der Namen Shrubs und Burton gebildet).

21 **carbon paper:** Kohle-, Durchschlagpapier.

porch. Twenty-six of them. My mom had to take them all back. She was cross.

Shrubs has a good rake, it is wood, not like ours which is green metal and boings. First we raked Shrubs' house and made piles in the street for a bon-fire, then we raked my house. My mom paid us a quarter, we bought Nik-O-Nips at Nick's. (Only it isn't Nick anymore, he died. Now it is Steve, who is foreign. He is mean. He wouldn't let me and Shrubs eat our peanut butter sandwiches in there when we ran away last time.)

After raking I went home for dinner. Mom said don't track up the living room. Then she said what a good job I did raking and I was a big boy, and she said that for being a good boy, Daddy would take me out after dinner and make a bonfire to roast marshmal-lows.

"Oh no, Mommy," I said. "Tonight is Devil's Night, for all the little goblins."

She said, "Oh my! I forgot!" But she said it like act-ing.

So after dinner Shrubs called for me and we went. It was dark. The streetlights were on. (I have never seen them go on, they are always just on.)

We rang doorbells. You run up real quiet and ring

---

4 **boing:** lautmalerischer Ausdruck für ein metallenes Geräusch; ge-meint sind die Zinken.
5f. **bonfire:** (Freuden-)Feuer.
7 **quarter:** 25-Cent-Stück.
   Nik-O-Nips: vermutl. erfundener Markenname für einen Riegel oder Snack.
13 **to track up a room:** Dreckspuren in einem Zimmer hinterlassen.
20f. **she said it like acting** (coll.): es klang geschauspielert.

the doorbell and run away and when the person in the
house answers the door there's nobody there. Ha ha.

I rang one and Shrubs watched. We both ran. Then
we both rang one. Then I told Shrubs to do one alone.
5 He said no, but I made him. He did. He went up to the
door. He rang the doorbell. But he didn't run. He just
stood there. I said run, but he stood there with his
hands in his pockets, he was froze. The door opened
and a man came out. He had a tie on. He said, "Yes,
10 what is it?" Shrubs didn't say anything. He stood just.
"What can I do for you?" said the man, but Shrubs just
looked at him. The man stood there for a minute, looking at Shrubs. "Who are you?" said the man. Shrubs
went like this with his shoulders. "Are you the paper
15 boy?" Shrubs said, "I don't know." Then the man went
inside. He closed the door. Shrubs just stood there.
Then the man opened the door and looked at Shrubs
again. Then he closed the door again. Then Shrubs left.

I asked Shrubs why he didn't run. He said he didn't
20 know why.

Mom made cookies for the Halloween party and put
them in a shoebox and tied it with a string and left it
on the yellow counter in the kitchen for me to take to
school. That night I went to bed and the Superman suit
25 was on the other bed in my room. My mom dyed long
underwear and it had a cape and an S and everything.
It looked like really Superman. I could hardly sleep.

The next morning I woke up all by myself, Mom
didn't wake me. I got up and washed and put on my

---

23 **counter:** Arbeitsplatte, -fläche (Küche).

Superman suit. I stood in front of the mirror and put my hands on my hips and made like the bullets bounced off. I made myself breakfast, it was orange juice and bread. I took the shoebox of cookies. I went. I didn't even wear
5 a coat because I was like Superman.

When I got to school there wasn't anybody there yet, so I stood outside and waited for the bell. I held the cookies extra tight so I wouldn't lose them. I stood and waited. Nobody came. I waited and waited. It was
10 cold. I held my cookies. Nobody came, I didn't know what to do.

Then the door of school opened and a man came out. He looked at me but I saw behind him inside, there were children in school, so I went in.

15 I went to Miss Iris' room but there were all different children there, not from my class. They looked at me. Miss Iris wasn't there. I stood next to her desk in my Superman suit and everybody looked at me and laughed.

20 Then Miss Iris came in. She said, "Why Burt, what are you doing here? The Halloween party was this morning. Your class is in Library now."

I went to Library and everybody looked at me because I was in my Superman suit. I forgot to bring any
25 other clothes. When I got home after school my mom said, "I'm sorry, Honey. I had an early beauty shop appointment this morning. I wrote a note for Jeffrey to wake you but I forgot to leave it. I found it in my purse at the beauty shop."

14

I have been at The Children's Trust Residence Center for three weeks now. I haven't been visited by my mommy and daddy because they aren't allowed yet, it
5 is the rules here. Dr Nevele says I'm not adjusted. I can't control myself. I have tantrums. He says that I am a good little boy who unfortunately does bad things sometimes. Like what I did to Jessica.

I am here by myself. I don't have any friends. I don't
10 know anybody hardly except Rudyard and Mrs Cochrane. No children. I have only been away from home once before (except for sleeping over at Shrubs' house). When I was five I went to camp.

It was entitled Little Camp Atinaka, for little kids. It
15 was far far away from our house, we drove, it took an hour. I sat on the hump all the way there. All the way there my mom told me how much fun it was going to be, just like on "Spin and Marty" on the Mickey Mouse Club. They have cowboy hats and ride horses.
20 (I love "Spin and Marty," man, they are swift, only I hate Mickey Mouse because he talks like a girl.)

Little Camp Atinaka lasted a week. They had cabins. Ours was Cabin Number One. We ate in the Arrowhead Lodge which was like school only no line. And
25 every day at lunch we sang a song.

---

5 **adjusted:** angepasst.
22 **cabin:** Blockhütte.

We are Cabin Number One
Number One, Number One
We are Cabin Number One
And we're the best of all.

5 Except we weren't. We stank at everything. Every
morning somebody peed in their bed, except me. I
never did.

Cabin Number One had two counselors, Miss Laurie
and Miss Sherry. They had very short hair but they
10 were girls. They slept in Cabin Number One with us
und they saw us when we got dressed and when we put
on our pajamas. I always got dressed under the covers
because I was embarrassed.

One day was Gold Rush Day, it was a special activ-
15 ity at camp. For the whole day everybody pretended
we looked for gold, which was rocks painted yellow.
One of the counselors dressed up as Sneaky Pete, and
went around shooting flour out of a gun at the
campers, and if he hit you, you were supposed to be
20 killed. I was scared of him, even though I knew he
wasn't real. He frightened me. And that night I woke
up in bed, it was very cold and I had to make. But I
was too afraid. I was afraid that Sneaky Pete was outside, and there wasn't a bathroom in Cabin Number
25 One. You had to go outside and walk down the hill. So
I held it. I held it and held it until I couldn't anymore,
and I made in my bed. I covered it with the sheets and
blanket, only it was very cold and it was wet and

---

5 **to stink at s.th.** (coll.): bei etwas sauschlecht sein.

8 **counselor:** Betreuer(in).

17 **sneaky:** gemein, hinterhältig.

soaked through. I had to lay on top of it. And the next morning everyone woke up and I was the only one who wet. Miss Laurie said the blanket was ruined, she had to throw it out. I wanted to be dead.

5   Now I am at The Children's Trust Residence Center, and I am all alone still. I don't have any friends. I wish Shrubs was here or even Marty Polaski. Sometimes I get letters from my mom and dad. Today I even got one from Jeffrey.

10   Dear Burt,
Hi Booger! How are you, I am fine. Mom told me I had to write you a letter so I am. (But I don't want to.) (Just kidding, ha ha.)
        Yesterday at school we had the Iowa Test. They gave it
15   to us in Homeroom. It took the whole entire day. I don't think you had it yet because you are still a pip squeak. They are to determine academic ability. They don't have normal questions and answers, instead we are to fill in the slot next to the best answer with a soft lead pencil, next
20   to a letter A, B, C, or D. Mr Lloyd told us how to cheat. You fill in all the slots because it's checked by a machine, only he said we'd get caught. He is an ass hole. I don't have to cheat anyway because I am an abnormally gifted pupil.
25   Mother told me I'm not supposed to tell anyone where you are. Everybody asks me. She told me to say you are

---

1   **to soak through:** durchsickern, -nässen.
    to lay (coll.): *to lie.*
11 **booger** (AE, slang): Typ, Kerl, Mann.
16 **pip squeak** (coll.): Pimpf, Winzling.
17 **academic ability:** schulische Begabung.
21 **slot:** Schlitz; hier: Kästchen.
23 **abnormally** (adv.): außergewöhnlich.

visiting relatives. Bruce Binder said you are in jail. Now
he thinks we have relatives in jail.

Where are you anyway? The day Mother and Dad took
you away, Jessica Renton's mother called here a hundred
times, but I didn't know what to say. I told her you were
visiting relatives.

Anyway, since you've been gone I haven't gone in your
room even once, so don't worry. Sophie said you left it in
a mess anyway, but I saw her yesterday in the basement,
she was holding your guitar you use to imitate Elvis and
she was crying.

Once in a while Mother asks me if I have any idea why
you did that to Jessica Renton. She gets all sad and I
don't know what to say. She says, "He's your brother, you
know him." And I say, "But you had him, not me." Also I
remember when we were little you used to beat me up almost every day even though I was older than you. Why
did you do that?

Last night Dad slapped me across the face at dinner for
saying the veal chops tasted like vomit. He was in one of
his moods, Mom said. He left the table and didn't come
back till after dinner. Remember last winter when he
wouldn't eat with us for a week and nobody ever found
out why?

Even though I hate your guts I wish you would hurry
up and come home, so you could help me take out the
trash, and also I don't have anybody to fool around with
on Sunday morning before anybody gets up.

Your Brother,
Jeffrey Rembrandt, Esquire.

---

20 **veal chop:** Kalbskotelett.
25 **to hate s.o.'s guts** (coll.): jdn. nicht verknusen, nicht ausstehen kön-
   nen.
27 **trash:** Müll.
30 **Esquire:** Herr (als Titel nach dem Namen).

But I still haven't got any letters from Jessica. Every day I ask Dr Nevele if they came and he doesn't say anything.

Yesterday Dr Nevele said that he wanted me to see some of the other doctors at The Children's Trust Residence Center, and that maybe if I went around with the other children I would make some new friends.

"We have many special rooms here," he said. "Rooms for learning to speak correctly, and rooms for acting out our feelings using playthings, and rooms for singing and playing and even doing gymnastics or wrestling."

I told him I wanted wrestling because I could pretend I am Dick the Bruiser. He is mean, man, but he has a flat top.

So I went.

First we had breakfast. It was eggs but it had like pieces of things in it, it was an omelet. I hated it. Also I had tomato juice which I think is blood when I drink it. But I didn't have a tantrum. I ate it just. Then we went.

First we had the Music Room. Everyone sits on the floor and sings "She'll Be Comin Round the Mountain When She Comes," and they make you go like this with your hands and yell "Whoa Back!" after you sing it. I felt like an idiot.

Then we had the Play Therapy Room, where I have already been once, with Rudyard. This time I played in

---

15 **Dick the Bruiser:** Name eines legendären Berufscatchers aus dem Mittleren Westen zwischen 1950 und 1980 (*to bruise:* quetschen, grün und blau schlagen).

the play kitchen they have. It has wood refrigerators and a stove that is pretend. I made Beef Stroganoff. My mom made it once. I hated it.

Then we went to Speech Therapy. It is for children who can't talk right, like Manny, he can't say L. But during the whole time in the Speech Therapy Room somebody in the back of the room kept talking, and they couldn't figure out who it was. It was me. I talked using ventriloquism which I learned out of a book in Library at school. It showed me how to make a puppet out of a paper bag. It was cool. Then I got my own dummy, I got him for Hanukah. I named him Bixby, which was stupid because I couldn't say his name in ventriloquism. So I killed him. I operated on his stomach because he had pleurodynia and all the stuffing came out and my mom gave him to the Good-will.

We got out of Speech Therapy. Then I saw someone in the hall, it was the postman, he had a bag he was taking letters into the office. I ran up to him and asked if there were any letters for me from Jessica. He didn't know what I was talking about. I said "Jessica Renton, she said she was going to write." But he just looked at me and said, "Well, I don't know anything about that." So I asked him again, because he's the postman, and he said, "Look, kid, I don't really care who writes who, I just have my job to do, so leave me alone," and then I

---

2 **to be pretend** (coll.): unecht sein.
9 **ventriloquism:** Bauchrednerei.
10 **puppet:** Marionette; (Hand-)Puppe.
12 **dummy:** Handpuppe (eines Bauchredners).
16f. **Goodwill:** karitative Sammlung.

lost control of myself. I screamed, "Give me some letters, give me some letters!" and I kicked him in the leg and started to hit him. I grabbed his bag away and it spilled all over the floor and I jumped on the letters
5 and started throwing them, looking for one from Jessica, and then he tried to grab me and I bit his hand. Everyone came out of the office and Dr Nevele grabbed me and pulled my arms around me and pulled me away to the Quiet Room, and I kept screaming to
10 give me letters.

He dragged me into the Quiet Room and pulled a chair in it from the hall and pushed me in the chair and took his belt off and put it around me. He left me there. He didn't say even anything.

15 I sat by myself. I didn't take the seatbelt off. I knew I couldn't control myself, my tantrum. I sat and sat. Then I took it off and walked real good citizenship back to Dr Nevele's office.

"I'm sorry," I said and gave him his belt back. He
20 looked at me funny, like he was embarrassed about something, and took his belt and said ok. I said, "I just wanted my letters, she said she was going to write them." Dr Nevele turned red when I said it. I don't know why. But he just nodded.

25 "I'm sorry, Burt," he said. It was like he was going to cry.

I went back to my wing. I layed down on my bed. I stayed there until it got dark outside. I looked up at the ceiling, which has little holes in it, like at school. I
30 missed dinner. Then I did something. I went over to the window and put my hands together and looked out and said

Star light star bright
First star I see tonight
I wish I may, I wish I might
Have the wish I wish tonight.

5 And I said for Jessica to please write me letters so I
would know that she was all right and that she remembered me.

Then I went to my bed and I layed down. I put my
head inside the pillow. There weren't any stars outside,
10 it was cloudy. And it was dark in my wing and I was all
alone. I heard thunder, it started to rain.

When I opened my eyes somebody was sitting next
to me smoking a cigarette, I saw the fire part in the
dark. I was frightened.

15 "Is anybody there?" I said.

"Sorry, did I wake you?" It was Rudyard. He blew
out smoke.

"No," I said.

"Where is everybody?"

20 "At Special Activities," I said. "A movie."

"Oh yeah."

Rudyard sat on the bed next to mine. My eyes got
used to the dark and I could see. He was bent over like
he was hurt of something.

25 I watched him. He didn't say anything. He got up
and walked around the room. He looked at things in
the dark. Then he went to the window and looked out,
and the light from the parking lot came behind him
and he was all black to me. He was an outline.

30 "You could say a wish upon a star, Rudyard," I said.
"You can order stuff."

"There aren't any stars." It was raining.

"I know."

He stood there looking anyway. Then he started to talk. He talked to himself.

"Sixteen years ago I was walking home from the grocery store down the alley behind my house. I used to go to the grocery store just to look around. I only had maybe fifteen cents but I'd shop all day, trying to decide what the very best thing I could buy for fifteen cents was. When I would finally decide and buy it, I really enjoyed it after all that.

I noticed that day at the grocery store they had a new display. It was for cookies. The kind that are chocolate on one side and chocolate stripes on the other. I hated them, actually, but they were good for dunking. They got just soggy enough without falling apart. This display had a picture of a boy on it, jumping. He was cut out of cardboard.

That day I decided to buy a bar of soap because it would last longer than candy. I was going to carve it when I got home. But on the way home it started to storm, the wind blew and the rain came down. I started to run but it caught me. I was pretty scared. I ducked under a tree behind the grocery store, in the middle of some bushes, to get out of the downpour. Then I noticed that someone had thrown out one of those displays, thrown it in the alley. The little cardboard boy had come loose. He was blowing against the bushes in the wind. His legs and arms were flapping and twisted, like he was throwing a tantrum.

---

15 **soggy:** eingeweicht, matschig.
19 **to carve:** einritzen, modellieren.
24 **downpour:** Regenguss.
28 **to flap:** schlaff herunterhängen.

I finally made it home. I just closed my eyes and ran.
On the way I dropped the soap. But to this day when I
walk along sometimes and look around, I think I see
cardboard boys throwing tantrums in the bushes. It's
just that the night reminds me."

He sat down again on the bed next to mine. I
watched the end of his cigarette. He didn't say anything for a long time. Then he said, "I think I'm going
to get fired, Burt. The Board of Directors has asked
me to leave."

15

After the Air Raid Drill it was only a week until
Thanksgiving vacation, I couldn't wait. I love Thanksgiving, it is a holiday but there isn't any praying and
5 you get to eat like crazy. I eat very much for my age. I
eat and eat. I eat more than anybody except Shrubs.
My dad says, "Even a train stops, Burt."

The day after Air Raid Drill we had elections for
Drinking Fountain Captain in Homeroom and I got
10 nominated by Bobby Cohen who I hardly know, it surprised me. We put our heads down and raised our
hands to vote, no peeking. I voted for Ruth Arnold because it is selfish to vote for yourself but Miss Iris said
you should, it shows you have confidence, but I think it
15 is bad manners.

I won. I was Drinking Fountain Captain for our
class. Every time we had lavatory time I got to stand
next to the drinking fountain and hold the handle
down and count to three-one-thousand and then tap
20 the children on the shoulder which means time's up. (I
give Shrubs extra though, and Marty Polaski said that
if Jessica was in our room I would let her drink up all
the water and everyone would die of thirst. I socked
him.)

25 Finally it was Thanksgiving vacation. That day after
school I saw Jessica walking out the Marlowe door but

12 **no peeking:** nicht gucken!

she didn't say anything to me so I didn't say anything. I watched her walk down Marlowe. Then suddenly she turned and waved at me. So I waved at her. We waved at each other. I smiled. Then she walked back
5 toward me. I was waving and smiling and waving and smiling, but she was waving at Marcie Kane who was standing behind me, not at me. I was embarrassed. I started to go. But then she said, "Don't say hi or anything, Burt."
10 I turned around. I said, "Ok, I won't." And I left.

That night I made a puppet. I built him out of pieces of wood my dad had in the basement. His arms were little ones and the rest of him were bigger ones. He had loops for elbows, they screwed in, and his head
15 was a ball that you make Christmas tree ornaments from, I got it from Shrubs last year. I painted him skin-colored with red circles on his cheeks. I made yarn for hair, and I sewed him a little suit with red shorts and a white shirt out of rags. I painted shoes on him. It took
20 me all night almost. My dad came down to see, but he let me stay up past my bedtime until I finished because there was no school the next day.

I named him Jerry the Puppet. When he was dry I took him upstairs to the kitchen. It was dark, and my
25 mom and dad were in bed. I folded up a dishtowel and put it on the yellow counter for his bed and then I folded up a washcloth and made it like a pillow for Jerry the Puppet. Then I went upstairs to bed but I thought of something and I came back down. I took

---

14 **loop:** hier: Schraubhaken mit Öse.
15 **ornament:** Schmuck, Verzierung.
17 **yarn:** Garn.

another dishtowel and made him a blankee so he wouldn't be cold. Then I kissed him.

"Goodnight, Jerry the Puppet," I said. "I'm glad I made you."

5 But the next morning I woke up extra early because it was Thanksgiving and I wanted to watch the parade on tv. I went downstairs and turned on Oral Roberts. (I like to watch him, he yells.) I had on my slippers with dog faces on them.

10 Jeffrey came down. I asked him if he wanted to play Three Stooges with me. I play it frequent with Shrubs. He is Curly. I am Moe. I bop him. Curly is my favorite, he is bald. He goes like this with his fingers, I can do it. Sometimes he is absent and they have Shemp. Shemp 15 looks like Moe only uglier. Sometimes I am him. But no one is Larry. No one ever wants to be Larry.

Jeffrey wouldn't play. Then the parade came on tv. It was exciting. It had floats. My favorite was Bullwinkle. Who is a moose. He is cartoons. I said, "Hi Bull-20 winkle!" He waved at me.

Then Mom and Dad got up, they had robes on and we had breakfast and we even got to eat in the den so we could watch the parade. We had pancakes and Little Boys' Coffee, which is coffee with mostly milk 25 and sugar in it for children. (I gave some pancakes to Jerry the Puppet but he wasn't hungry.) Then Mom started cooking Thanksgiving dinner.

---

1 **dishtowel:** Geschirrtuch.
11 **stooge:** jd., der tut, was ihm gesagt wird.
12 **to bop s.o.:** jdm. einen leichten Schlag versetzen.
18 **float:** Festwagen.
24 **little boys' coffee:** Michkaffee, Muckefuck.

We have company on Thanksgiving, it is uncles and aunts and cousins on my mom's side. My dad has a side too only not on Thanksgiving. His side is for Passover. We go to Bubbie's house. She is my grand-
5 mother. Her name is Bubbie. She is very old and talks Jewish which I don't understand, only sometimes she talks English which I still don't understand. I feel she should have subtitles. She calls me Baby Cocker because once I went over in my Davy Crockett suit. I
10 don't have a Zadie on my dad's side. He is passed away, I never even saw him except pictures. He looks like my dad only brown because of the picture. On my mom's side I have a grandfather. He is named Gramps. It is Gramps on my mom's side and Zadie on my dad's
15 side, only Gramps isn't dead. Only I don't have a Bubbie on my mom's side, she is dead. Her name was Grandma. It is very confusing. I think Gramps should marry Bubbie. They could go to a restaurant and talk Jewish to each other.
20 For Thanksgiving my mom made turkey. She also made stuffing which I helped her make, I tore up toast. Also she made candy sweet potatoes which are sweet potatoes only like candy and they have a cherry on top which I don't like so I give them to Jeffrey who gives
25 them to Cleo our dog and she eats them and pukes. This is how we celebrate Thanksgiving.

---

1 **company:** Gäste, Besuch.
3f. **Passover:** jüdisches Passahfest, das in etwa dem christlichen Oster-
   fest entspricht.
8 **subtitle:** Untertitel.
9 **Davy Crockett:** legendärer Jäger und Fallensteller im amerikanischen Westen des 19. Jh.s.
10 **zadie** (Yidd.): guter, frommer Mann; Großvater.

After breakfast my dad said, "How would you fellows like to go see Santa Claus today?"

I said, "No thanks."

"Why?" said Dad.

5 "Because we're Jewish," I said. "It's wrong."

"Just get dressed, Burt, don't worry about it," he said. But I folded my arms up and wouldn't, I frowned.

So Dad came over and said, "Burt, Santa Claus is for everyone. He is all religions, now hurry up or we'll
10 be late."

I said, "So he's Jewish?"

"Yeah," said Dad. "He's Jewish, ok. Let's go." So we went.

Santa was at the Ford Rotunda, it is a big building
15 that's round. It is far. It has cars in it. I asked my dad how Santa got there so fast when I just saw him on tv in the parade downtown and he said he took a helicopter.

At the Ford Rotunda was Santa's Magic Forest. It
20 had lights and trees with colors on them, you walk through and there are elves that are statues that move like real elves. Also they had a part with reindeers, you could pet them. I couldn't see the part they have on them for flying, I think it goes in like. I fed one of them
25 a peanut. He ate it. He was brown.

Then we went to see Santa. He was at the end. There was a big line, it went around and around, you couldn't even see Santa. We waited and waited. Then we got there. Jeffrey went first, he sat on Santa and

14 **rotunda:** Rotunde, Rundbau (meist mit einer Kuppel).
21 **elf** (pl. *elves*): Kobold, Elfe.
22 **reindeer:** Rentier(e).

said, "I want you to buy me a model Thunderbird, you can get it at Maxwell's, ok?"

Santa said, "Ho ho."

(I feel Santa is phony baloney because he laughs all the time and I don't know what's so funny, to be candid.)

Then Jeffrey said, "I would also like a cowboy shirt and pants and boots with real spurs on them."

Santa said, "Ho ho."

Then Jeffrey got off.

I started to walk away but Dad grabbed my hand and pulled me back. I said, "No I have to fix something," but he said come on. So I sat on Santa. He was hot.

"Where's Blitzen?" I said.

"Blitzen who?" he said.

"You know."

He said, "Ho ho."

"Are you Jewish?" I said.

Santa didn't say anything.

"Are you?"

Then he said, "Well, I don't know. Well, yes, I guess Santa Claus is all religions. I guess I am."

All the parents started to take their children out of line. They heard. Santa said, "I didn't mean that," but pretty soon there wasn't anybody left. My dad grabbed me and we went.

It was warm for Thanksgiving, it didn't even snow, and by the time we got home it was raining. My mom was still cooking dinner, it smelled an aroma and my

---

12 f. **I have to fix something** (coll.): ich hab was zu erledigen.

daddy read the newspaper and Jeffrey looked at a magazine.

I said, "Mom, how come they don't have Jessica in the phone book?"

5 "Who's that, Honey?"

"Jessica, a girl."

"They only have daddies' names in the phone book, Sweetheart, last names," she said.

I took it out and turned to Renton, it was like a dic-
10 tionary, I could use it, and there was only one Renton on Marlowe.

I am scared of telephones because once the operator came on and yelled at me for dialing too slow, but I dialed the telephone then. I wanted to tell Jessica that
15 Santa Claus was Jewish.

It rang. Then it stopped. Then it rang, then it stopped.

A girl answered, she said, "Hello?"

"Is this Jessica?" I said, I was nervous, man. "This is
20 Burt from school."

But her voice was wrong, it didn't sound like Jessica, and I deduced that she was crying.

"Oh Burt," she said. "My daddy is dead."

12 **operator:** (Telefon-)Vermittlung.

16

Rain says a noise: Shh. You can hear it when it comes down. It is God telling us to be quiet.

On the afternoon of Thanksgiving I kneeled back-
5 wards on the couch in the living room of our house and looked out the window across the street at the Nemsicks who came out of their house with news-papers over their heads and got inside their car. They were all dressed up. They were laughing. But the
10 motor in their car cried and smoke came out and I thought, They are going to a funeral, which is a party without presents.

From the living room I could smell the kitchen where Mom cooked dinner. The table in the dining
15 room had the good tablecloth on it and the good plates from the china cabinet which I am not allowed to touch. There were the good glasses and the silverware with flowers on the ends and napkins made out of cloth, not paper, like little baby tablecloths.
20 I looked out the window at the street. Rain fell down in little torpedoes on the cars and made splash-ing like fog on them. It made lines on the windows, like clear finger painting. I raced two raindrops down. I put my nose against the glass and made fog donuts by

---

16 **china cabinet:** Geschirrschrank.
17 **silverware:** Silberbesteck.
21 f. **splashing:** Spritzer.
24 **donut** (AE): Krapfen in Kringelform.

breathing and Martian footprints which you make with your hand, it looks like Martians have been walking on the window pane, trying to get out.

I went to the hall closet. I took out my raincoat and boots and put them on.

My raincoat is yellow, it is like a banana peel on the outside. It has cloth on the inside with sailboats on it. There is a hat too, it has a hole for my face. The sleeves on my raincoat are too long, but my mom says I will grow into it. They hang over my hands.

My boots are rubber with like tires on the bottom so I don't fall down. They have snaps that jingle and I can't do them right because I am little.

Inside my raincoat I had somebody with me, he had on red shorts and yarn for hair. Jerry the Puppet, I had him with me.

Inside the hall closet also was my father's coat, I had wore it to see Santa and there was somebody in the pocket of it too. It was Monkey Cuddles, I took him to see Santa Claus. He told me that Jessica was very sad but he couldn't go because he was in my dad's pocket, cooking dinner.

I opened the front door. I went.

The rain made thumps on my rain hat that sounded like drums, but my mom says that rain is fairies dancing on the roof, and sometimes I do something when

---

1 **Martian:** Mars-; Marsbewohner.
3 **window pane:** Fensterscheibe.
4 **hall closet:** Garderobe(nschrank).
12 **snap:** Schnalle.
   to jingle: hier: in hellem Ton klappern.
18 **wore:** *worn.*
24 **thump:** Klopfen.

148

nobody sees, I open the window and put a towel on the window sill and say, "You can come in, fairies, I will turn off the light so I can't see you."

The sidewalk on Lauder is made out of squares of cement with like filling in between. It goes down Lauder and turns the corner. I followed it. I was going somewhere, I turned down Clarita and looked at the houses. Inside them I saw people watching television and some of them had decorations in the windows with tinsel around them and one house had a shoebox scene in the window, like I make at school sometimes. This one had hay and camels and sheeps and a baby in it with a gold fan around his head. (Once I made a shoebox scene for extra credit for Social Studies. I wanted a B so my mom wouldn't be disappointed. It was Benjamin Franklin. I cut him out of the *Golden Book Encyclopedia* and folded his feet so he stood up. I named it "Benjamin Franklin Stands Up." I got a C anyway.)

I turned down Marlowe. The trees usually make like a tunnel, they touch almost, but now they were bald. It looked like they were shaking hands over the street, but they couldn't reach because Jessica's father died.

---

2 **window sill:** Fenstersims.
10 **tinsel:** Lametta.
  shoebox scene: Weihnachtskrippe in einem Schuhkarton.
13 **gold fan:** goldener Fächer; gemeint ist ein Heiligenschein aus Goldpapier.
14 **for extra credit:** als Fleißarbeit für eine bessere Note.
15 **B:** (Note) Gut.
16 **Franklin:** Benjamin F. (1706–90), amerikanischer Politiker, Wissenschaftler und Erfinder.
16f. **encyclopedia:** Enzyklopädie, großes Nachschlagewerk.
18 **C:** (Note) Befriedigend.

And then I was at Jessica's house, with blue shutters.
I stopped in front of it. I stood and looked. The front
door was open. There was a walk up to it, like we have,
and there was an R on the screen door like we have.
Exactly. I stood in front on the sidewalk, in my raincoat, and watched.

The driveway was full of cars, they had license plates
on them that said "Michigan, the Water Wonderland."

Jessica's house had a lamp post on the lawn, it
looked like a little streetlight. You never see streetlights go on. They are always just on. The lamp post on
Jessica's lawn was on. I stood and watched it.

A dog came up to me. He was wet. He was beige.
He came out of the bushes from the house next door
and went on Jessica's lawn and smelled her bushes and
then went in them and made. He came over to me. He
sat down right next to me and watched Jessica's house.
We watched it together. Then he went.

Jessica's house has awnings, they looked like eyelids,
and the rain came down them and I thought, Her
house is crying too. But I stayed right where I was in
case she needed me or something.

The front door opened. A man and a lady came out.
They had a big umbrella. They had hats. They had
black clothes on, because it was a funeral. Jeffrey told
me you wear black so it'll be dark and the dead person
won't wake up. The man and the lady came down the
front walk. They almost walked into me. They got in
the last car on the driveway, and started it. Then they

---

4 **screen door:** Fliegengittertür.
7 **license plate:** Nummernschild (Auto).
19 **awning:** Markise.

rolled down the window and said, "Can I help you, little boy?"

"No I'm just looking," I said.

I watched them drive away to Seven Mile Road
5 where there was a lot of traffic, you could see there
was spray from the cars in the rain and noise. I am not
allowed to cross Seven Mile. It is too busy. It has lines
painted on it and there are stores not houses.

I waited in front of Jessica's house. I looked out the
10 hole of my rain hat. The house next door's front door
opened and two children came out. It was Roger and
Joey Lester, I knew them from school, they are twins
but don't look alike. They looked at me but they didn't
know it was me because of the rain hat. I didn't say
15 anything. They walked down Marlowe. I never knew
they lived there, but sometimes Shrubs plays with
them. He said they are poor. They don't have any toys,
so they play with their socks.

Jessica's house has a tree in front. A monkey
20 jumped out of it and landed on my shoulder and told
me in monkey language that there were natives on
Seven Mile Road who were coming to kill Jessica, so I
put my hand around my mouth and gave the call and
all the elephants came and scared them away. The
25 monkey said thanks. He went.

Mom said rain is when God fixes his water faucet.
She said that God sees everything so I better be good.
I asked her if God knows how Milky the Clown does
his magic tricks on "Milky's Party Time," on tv. (Some-
30 times I wave at God. He sees me. He is my friend be-

---

6 **spray:** Spritzwasser, Gischt.
26 **water faucet:** Wasserhahn.

cause once I prayed for the Tigers to win and they did.)

I stood in front of Jessica's. I smelled my raincoat, it smells like a tent when it gets wet. (Once I was
5 in a tent, at Northland at Bill's Sporting Goods, they had some and I went in. It was like camping out. It smelled.)

Then a truck pulled up to Jessica's. It was blue. It said "Paul's Fine Food" on the side, somebody painted
10 it. A man got out and he went around and opened a door in the back and took out a big tray with food on it. He went up the front walk into Jessica's house. I looked at the truck. I thought, I could steal the truck and rescue Jessica and drive to Florida, but the man
15 came back. He looked at me.

"Hey, kid, you lost or something?"

I didn't say a reply.

"You ought to get in out of the rain. It ain't healthy, kid," he said.
20 "You shouldn't say ain't," I told him, but he didn't hear me, he was gone.

I looked at all the windows in Jessica's house. I thought maybe she saw me, she was watching me, but I didn't see her, but maybe she was, they were all foggy.
25 I stayed anyway.

Roger and Joey Lester came back, they had a bag, I deduce they were shopping. They looked at me again and I did this with my hand only they didn't wave back. They went in their house and shut the door.

---

8 **to pull up:** anhalten (Auto).
18 **ain't:** *isn't.*
24 **foggy:** beschlagen (Fenster).

The wind made the rain go like in curves on the street, and blew inside my hat, I looked out the hole. A branch fell down from the tree behind me. A squirrel ran inside a tree. A car went past. A door slammed
5 down the block. A newspaper blew past me. Somebody yelled, "Collect for the *News*." An airplane went in the sky. On Seven Mile Road there was almost an accident. It started to get dark. It was almost night. I stood in front of Jessica's. I stood and watched.

10 A man went into her house with flowers. An old woman came out with plastic over her hair to keep it dry. Another lady opened the front door and looked at me but she just shook her head and went back in.

Then it was dark. I saw that the streetlights were on
15 but I still didn't see them go on. I took Jerry the Puppet and walked on Jessica's lawn up to the little lamp post on her grass. I put him at the bottom of it, and then I took off my rain hat and put it over him like a little tent for Jerry the Puppet.

20 I looked one more time at her house, and then I started to walk home, it was still raining and I didn't have my rain hat but I didn't care. I was thinking about something else maybe. I had on my raincoat. The sleeves hung over my hands.

25 When I got home my mom was very angry.

"How dare you walk out of here without telling anyone. You've had us worried sick," she said. "And you've made dinner get cold, we all waited for you, look at the time. Where have you been?"

30 I took off the raincoat and hung it neatly in the

---

27 **you've had us worried sick** (coll.): wir haben uns wegen dir schreckliche Sorgen gemacht.

153

closet. I took off my boots (my shoes stuck inside them like always, I had to pull them out separate). I put my boots away.

There were many people in my house. There was noise and cigar smoke from my uncles.

I walked up the stairs to my room. I closed the door. I layed down on my bed. I looked out the window.

I got up. I sat on the other bed. I got up again. I went and sat at my desk. I got up again. I walked over to my closet. I opened the door. I went in and closed the door.

17

On Monday morning after Thanksgiving vacation I woke up and everything was different. Outside was drizzling and I looked at it and thought, Nothing is the same now. I looked at my cowboy lamp, one of the cowboys was playing a harmonica, I knew it was taps.

My mom came into my room while I was putting on my pants and she saw my peenie and I yelled. She said, "My God, I'm your mother, aren't I?" And I said no (because I think I am adopted).

But she made breakfast like always and swallowed loud like always and then Shrubs called on me and while I was getting my coat he went in the den and stole candy out of the glass thing.

It was like I hadn't gone to school in a long time. On the way I thought that Jessica wouldn't be there but I would be in her room because she has Miss Iris for belltime and I was going to make Miss Iris a new Christmas bulletin board. But Jessica would be absent because you are allowed when somebody dies. (Once I was. Sophie's sister died and I went to the funeral, it was a little church downtown with all colored negroes in it except us. Mom had to run up to the front and hug Sophie, she cried so hard.)

---

4 **drizzling:** Nieselregen.
6 **harmonica:** Mundharmonika.
  taps (pl.): Zapfenstreich.

"Do you want the orange ones or the grape ones?"
said Shrubs. He pulled out some candy, but he couldn't
take the cellophane off because he was wearing his
hockey gloves. He always wears them, they are giant.
5 They have pads on them all the way up and the fingers
are real big, you can put two in one and then make like
one of your fingers fell off. I took a grape one, it was a
hand grenade.

(I lost my gloves. I always do. I don't know where
10 they go. Mom says, "They don't just get up and walk
away," and I say, "No, mine drove, they went to
Florida for the winter like Aunt Fran and Uncle Les."
She says, "Don't open up your mouth." She even
bought me things that clip on my jacket so you don't
15 lose your gloves. I lost my jacket. My mom said I
would lose my head if it weren't screwed on but I said
I would find it easy because I know what it looks like,
only mirrors make you backwards.)

I went right to Miss Iris' room to make the bulletin
20 board. I sat in the back, I didn't even have to listen. I
got one of the new desks, they have hard stuff on the
top like a kitchen. I like new desks, they are smooth
and you don't have to put paper under your paper because of marks.

25 For the bulletin board I got to use real glue, not
paste, and pointy scissors which could put an eye out. I
started on the beard. I made it with cotton that I got
from the office in a first-aid kit. But the glue spilled

---

1 **grape:** hier: mit Traubengeschmack.
5 **pads** (pl.): Polsterung.
18 **mirrors make you backwards** (coll.): im Spiegel sieht man sich falsch rum.
28 **first-aid kit:** Erste-Hilfe-Kasten.

and it went all over me and the desk and the cotton stuck to everything. I started sneezing and everybody looked at me.

The tardy bell rang. Then something happened. Jessica walked in.

She was dressed up, with knee socks and a dress and shiny shoes with windows on the tops. She was tardy but Miss Iris just went like this with her head which meant sit down. On the way to her desk Jessica looked at me. I had cotton on me everywhere.

"Class, today we're going to have a special Show and Tell," said Miss Iris. "We'll take turns telling what we did over Thanksgiving vacation. It will be fabulous."

(I felt very weird because I was in a different class and because Jessica was there and because I was covered with cotton and because Miss Iris said fabulous.)

"Andy Debbs, would you like to begin?"

(I started on the nose. It was going to be round like a bowl full of jelly. I made a circle, but it wasn't round, so I trimmed it but it still wasn't, so I trimmed it again and it fell apart. I drew another one on construction paper but I couldn't get it round. I tried again, then I crushed it. I broke my pencil with a karate chop. Andy Debbs told about his Thanksgiving.)

"First off, we all went to chapel to say our prayers with the sisters to thank the Good Lord for seeing us

---

4 **tardy bell:** zweites Klingeln zum Zeichen des Unterrichtsbeginns.
12 **to take turns doing s.th.:** sich dabei abwechseln, etwas zu tun.
14 **weird:** komisch, seltsam.
22f. **construction paper:** Zeichenpapier, -karton.
24 **karate chop:** Karateschlag.
26 **first off** (coll.): zuerst, als Erstes.

safe through another Thanksgiving, but Petey Woods
wouldn't come because he broke his leg on the swingset two weeks ago and wasn't thankful.

It was raining outside, so after chapel we got to go to
the Commons, where they had some Christmas trees
for us to decorate. The older kids had to watch over
the little ones, though, so it wasn't much fun because
they pick on us. We had two trees this year, one was
from Brickman's Hardware and one was from the
Torch Drive. We used the same ornaments as last year
but some of them was broke. The sisters even helped.
Father Birney came down too, it was an honor.

Then we had Thanksgiving dinner. It was special because they put tablecloths on the tables in the Dining
Hall. We had turkey and dressing and dessert. We
could get seconds too.

Then we went back to the Commons and played
games. Then we said some prayers and Father Birney
talked to us about how we're graced by the grace of
God to have such wonderful sisters taking care of us
and how he cried because he had no shoes until he met
a boy who had no feet, and then we went to bed but I
got out of brushing my teeth because I put Parcheesi
away."

(I got it right finally, I took three little circles that I

2f. **swingset:** Schaukelgerüst.
5 **Commons** (pl.): Gemeindesaal.
12 **Father:** Anrede für einen katholischen Geistlichen.
16 **seconds** (pl., coll.): Nachschlag.
19 **to be graced:** (Gottes) Gnade erfahren.
23 **to get out of doing s.th.** (coll.): sich darum drücken, etwas zu tun.
    Parcheesi: klassisches Brettspiel, auch »The Royal Game of India«
    genannt.

traced from nickels and put them together so it looked like a nose almost and then I glued it and it slipped but I just left it.)

Miss Iris called on Ruth Arnold. She was all smiley, like an idiot. She started to talk only no one could hear her. She is the ugliest person in America, no lie. When she was born her parents said what a treasure, so they buried her. She has to sneak up on a glass of water, her nose runs from her. (These are jokes.) Eugene Larson yelled, "Turn up the volume switch!" and Miss Iris made Ruth Arnold stop until we settled down.

"For Thanksgiving vacation," said Ruth Arnold, "we went to Philadelphia, Pennsylvania, to visit my Aunt Greta. Philadelphia is the home of many historic sites." She reached in her pocket and took out a piece of paper. She started to read.

"There is stately Independence Hall, where our forefathers signed the Declaration of Independence back in 1776."

Eugene Larson started coughing. He fell off his desk and started to roll on the floor like he was going to die, and everybody laughed and Miss Iris went and grabbed his collar and marched him right out of the room. Ruth Arnold kept talking though. You couldn't hear her anyway.

Jessica turned around and looked at me. I saw her. I looked down and pretended like I was making the nose again.

Miss Iris came in and slammed the door and said for

---

1 **to trace:** hier: durch Umkreisen abmalen.
  nickel (AE): 5-Cent-Stück.
10 **volume switch:** Lautstärkeknopf.

everyone to put their heads down until we could control ourselves. Ruth Arnold was still reading off her paper.

"That's enough, Ruth, sit down," said Miss Iris. "Class, put those heads down and I mean now!"

I didn't know what to do. I didn't know if it meant me. I raised my hand to ask but Miss Iris didn't see me, so I went up to her desk but I stopped halfway and turned around and Jessica was staring at me and then I just stood there.

"Burt, what are you doing? What in the world are you doing?" said Miss Iris.

I walked up to her desk.

"Miss Iris, should I put my head down too?"

"No."

I went back to my desk and started on the mouth.

"All right, people," said Miss Iris. "If you think you can control your mouths, you may pick your heads up quietly and we'll continue. Sit down, Ruth, you had your chance."

Then Jessica raised her hand. Miss Iris saw her but didn't say anything. Jessica stood up anyway and went to the front of the classroom.

She smiled. I thought she was going to sing. She smoothed out her dress and pushed her hair back and stood up very good posture. Then she started to talk, not too loud, not too soft. Just right.

"On Thanksgiving morning I woke up quite early to find a surprise as I looked out my bedroom window. I discovered that I could see all the way to Montana.

---

26 **very good posture:** in tadelloser Haltung.

And I saw my horse, Blacky, running, his mane blew in
the wind and there was dust around his hooves. He
was running to me.

I got dressed and went outside. Nobody else was up
yet, and the sun was shining like summer. I didn't need
wraps. I walked out on our front porch where we have
flowers even in winter and there was a boy on the walk
with a raincoat on. I said, 'Why do you have a raincoat
on, boy? It isn't raining.' And he gave me a puppet.
Then we went for a walk.

We went to a long sidewalk and slid down a chute to
a place where there were lots of toys. There were dolls
and models and Raggedy Anns. Then we went to a
place where there were rides and we went on them, we
were the only ones. Then we went on a boat.

We found a car, it had the keys in it and we drove to
Florida for three hours. When we came back we put on
a play about policemen. Then we were very tired so we
went to my house and did magic tricks until we fell
asleep and when we woke up we were grown."

Nobody said anything.

I looked at her with my eyes. I couldn't not look.
She stared at the back of the room where there was a
bulletin board with turkeys on it that I made. And
under my stomach I felt someone twist me like an airplane with rubber bands, tighter and tighter.

---

6 **wrap** (coll.): Jacke, Mantel.
11 **chute:** Rutsche, Rutschbahn.
13 **Raggedy Ann:** populäre Flickenpuppe; die Puppenfiguren Raggedy
   Ann und Raggedy Andy wurden von Johnny Gruelle (1880–1938)
   geschaffen (vgl. *ragdoll* ›Flickenpuppe‹).
14 **ride:** Karussell.
26 **rubber band:** Gummiband.

Nobody even moved. Miss Iris didn't move. But I stood up all by myself and walked to the front of the room. I looked at Jessica. She looked at me and turned to the door. She opened it. She walked out the door and I followed her.

18

Jessica went out the Marlowe door right past the hall monitors. I could hardly keep up, and she ran across Curtis and started down Marlowe, walking fast toward her house. It was very cold out, but it was a whole block before I remembered we didn't have any wraps on. It still drizzled rain. Ahead of me I saw it on Jessica's hair, it stuck and made like diamonds.

The street was empty. There weren't even any safety boys because they were all still in school. (When they take off their belts they turn into real children again. Once I saw the grease safety from Lauder at Northland with his mother and she yelled at him for picking his nose. It was like he wasn't even him.)

Jessica turned the corner at Margarita. She wasn't going to her house after all, I deduced it.

"We better go back," I called after her. "We don't have any wraps and this being the flu season, we better."

But she kept walking faster and faster like she was hurrying somewhere. I didn't know where. Then I thought something. That she was trying to get away from me, because she never asked me to come. So I stopped on the sidewalk, and put my arms around me because it was so cold, and watched her get smaller down the street.

2 f. **hall monitor:** Überwachungsmonitor im Foyer.
18 **flu:** Kurzform von *influenza:* Grippe.

But she stopped. She turned around, and yelled, "Come on, it's freezing!"

I ran. But I tripped and scraped my chin and it was embarrassing because she saw.

5 "We have to get coats," she said.

"No lie," I said.

Then I saw him. The truant officer. He was leaning on a car a block from my house, he had a hat pulled over his eyes and a pad that he was writing on, the
10 names of all the children who play hookey from school and our names were on it. He was waiting near my house to catch us. I took Jessica's arm.

"It's the truant officer, Jessica," I said. "He'll get us and send us to reform school. What'll we do?"

15 Jessica looked at him.

"Burt, he's just reading the water meter."

"Oh."

We walked toward my house.

El Commandante came to school and tied up Miss
20 Messengeller in the office until she told him where they kept the money from the lunchroom. Then I came in the office because I had a conniption fit in Social Studies and I saw him and socked the Commandante but the other soldiers captured me but I escaped by
25 ventriloquism and killed El Commandante with my sword so they expelled me for bad citizenship. Jessica helped me.

---

7 **truant officer:** Schulangestellter, der Schulschwänzer dingfest macht.
9 **pad:** Notizblock.
10 **to play hockey from school** (coll.): die Schule schwänzen.
14 **reform school:** Besserungsanstalt.
16 **water meter:** Wasserzähler.
26 **to expel:** (von der Schule) verweisen.

164

This is what I was going to tell my mother when she asked me what I was doing home.

"Don't say anything to my mother," I told Jessica. "She is deaf, so she can't hear you. You have to use sign language."

But nobody was home. I had to climb through the milk chute to get in, which I do frequent. There was milk in it. No chocolate. I squeezed through. I am good at squeezing. Once my dad said why don't I put myself in an envelope and mail myself to Alaska but I said I didn't have enough stamps. (I didn't.)

I went through the kitchen to the back hall and opened the door for Jessica. She was shivering. She just stood in the back hall and shook all over and suddenly I thought she was going to die, so I ran up to my room and got blankee. I put him on Jessica. He was very glad.

Then I went to the front hall closet. It was very quiet in the house, you could hear the clock tick in the living room, and I got a little afraid because I wasn't supposed to be there then. I opened the hall closet and got Dad's jacket out, the one I wore to the Ford Rotunda to see Santa Claus. I felt a lump in the pocket, it was Monkey Cuddles, he was having lunch in the pocket. Also I took out my mom's coat that she wears shopping. I took them to the back hall and put my mom's coat on Jessica over blankee and put my dad's coat on me. The sleeves hung over my hands. Monkey Cuddles was singing.

Soon Jessica stopped shivering. She held on to blankee under the coat. He liked it.

13 **to shiver:** zittern, schlottern.

165

I told her we had to go or we'd get in trouble when my mom came home.

We went.

We started walking toward Seven Mile Road, the other way from school. (I thought I would never go to school again. I was right.)

We passed Shrubs' house on the corner next to the car wash. There wasn't any cars in it though, because it was inclement weather, but there were two colored men sitting on the bench outside. They ate potato chips. They had on black aprons that were rubber. One of them I saw before, he is always there, he looks mean because his nose goes like down, but once Shrubs said he was locked out of his house and he went to the car wash and the man let him stay there and gave him potato chips and he didn't even have to help.

We turned this way on Seven Mile. Left. This way is right, this way is left, this way is down, this way is up. If you get lost you should ask a policeman, and if you can't brush after every meal, swish and swallow. I am a fountain of information. My dad said so.

Then we came to Maxwell's. In Maxwell's there are two women who work there. One is young and small with dark hair who is nice to children. The other one is old with gray hair who is mean and Jeffrey calls her the old battleaxe. She even has her glasses on a chain around her neck so they can't get away. She was the only one in Maxwell's that day.

---

9 **inclement:** unfreundlich, hässlich (Wetter).
11 **apron:** Schürze, Schurz.
20 **to swish one's mouth:** den Mund ausspülen.
26 **battleaxe** (pej., fig.): Kneifzange, Drachen (Person).

Maxwell's smells an aroma like new shoes, it is the toys (they all have new shoes on them). Jessica went to the doll part because she is a girl and I went to the cowboys. They are on a special shelf all by themselves
5 where children can't reach. They are in color. I have some of them, even Zorro, but I always look at them in Maxwell's because they have guns and hats on them that come off and I lost them on mine.

There was a new one on the shelf, I recognized him
10 right away, Hopalong Cassidy. I don't like him because he is too old to be a cowboy, he has white hair like Gramps. I feel he should retire to Borman Hall where Gramps lives, it is like a hospital where you stay while you're dying but it's kosher. But I like Hopalong Cas-
15 sidy's suit, it is black with like nails in it. Jeffrey got a Hopalong Cassidy bike for his birthday. It was black with like nails in it.

The old battleaxe snuck up behind me and said, "May I help you, little boy?"
20 I jumped a mile.

I said, "I am buying toys for my children. I have two sons, Burt and Don Diego. They are splendid little boys, oh my. They won the Spelling B."

The old battleaxe wore the same perfume as Mrs
25 Marston the kindergarten teacher who you could smell for a mile, it smells like pie.

I walked over to the baseball part. "Nice mitts," I said. Then a man walked into Maxwell's and the old battleaxe went to see him.

---

18 **snuck** (AE): *sneaked.*
20 **I jumped a mile** (coll.): ich bekam einen Riesenschreck.
27 **mitts:** (Baseball-)Handschuhe.

It was the truant officer. I ducked under the bats.

"You'll have to bring them around the back, I can't have you tracking up the floor, the girl just waxed," said the old battleaxe to the truant officer. He went
5 out the front door to come around the back. He was bringing the cages around the back and they'd chase us into them.

I picked up a bat.

The old battleaxe came back to the baseball part
10 looking for me but I wasn't there, I was behind the balsa-wood counter where they sell Boy Scout projects. I sat on the floor with my bat. I couldn't let them take us, I couldn't let them take Jessica.

I smelled the old battleaxe. I held on to my bat. She
15 walked up next to me and stopped. Everything was silence.

Then I jumped up screaming, "It's a trap! It's a trap!" and swung the baseball bat over my head. "You'll never take us alive!" I yelled.
20 The truant officer walked in the back door and I ran up to him swinging my bat screaming "Yah, yah, yah," and ran out the back door, past him, up and down the sidewalk behind Maxwell's, jumping up and down with the bat.
25 Then the truant officer put some boxes in Maxwell's and got in his truck and left.

I stopped jumping up and down. I was outside Maxwell's by myself and he was gone. I went back in.

"This one's a little too light," I said. "I better buy
30 something else."

---

11 **balsa-wood:** Balsaholz (sehr leichte Holzart).
11 f. **projects:** hier: Sachen, Zubehör.

I went to the stuffed animals part. Jessica was still looking at the dolls. Maxwell's has many stuffed animals from which to choose from. I used to have a big Panda, he was my favorite besides Monkey Cuddles,
5 but he drowned when our basement flooded. My favorite one at Maxwell's is the kangaroo because he has a baby in his pouch that really comes out and you get both. Also they had a walrus with teeth.

"I think perhaps I'll buy one of these kangaroos
10 here," I said to the old battleaxe, "only I'm still looking too because it's outrageous."

She followed me all over Maxwell's. The sleeves from my dad's coat kept catching on things and knocking them off the shelves.

15 "Young man," the old battleaxe finally said, "unless you have money to buy something, you'll have to leave. We can't have children in here alone without supervision."

But I wasn't alone, Jessica was with me. I got angry
20 at the old battleaxe, and started to cry almost, until Jessica started talking from the doll section.

"This isn't the real Raggedy Ann," she said. "The real Raggedy Ann had buttons for eyes, not plastic. Why don't you have a real one here, Ma'am?"

25 "That is a real one, young lady," said the old battleaxe. "Now you and your brother will have to leave."

"No I'm sorry," said Jessica. "That isn't the real one. I had the real one and she is dead. She died with my father in the hospital the day before Thanksgiving."

---

7 **pouch:** Beutel (des Känguruhs).
8 **walrus:** Walross.
11 **outrageous:** unverschämt, horrend teuer.

For a minute the old battleaxe didn't know what to do, she stared at Jessica and played with her glasses. Then she said, "Goodbye, children," and took our hands and pulled us toward the front door. Jessica
5 pulled away.

"You know, Ma'am, it just so happens that today is a holiday in our religion and my brother and I came here to buy toys, which you are supposed to do on this holiday. It is more blessed to give than to receive you
10 know. But now we can't, because you won't let us stay here. I think that's very sad for you, Ma'am. Very sad." And she walked out of Maxwell's by herself.

"You better pray," I said, and followed her out.

We walked up Seven Mile Road together, and Jes-
15 sica didn't say anything else. She was good at fibbing though, you could tell.

"Streets are different colors, Jessica," I said. "Seven Mile Road is black with white stripes and Lauder is gray and Marlowe has stones in it. I think it's very in-
20 teresting." Then I saw a man walking down Seven Mile in front of us, as he walked away he got smaller. We learned it in Science, it is because the world is round. I told Jessica about it.

"Yes," she said. "But what if it isn't? It would be like
25 when they run the Air Raid sirens on Saturday as a test. Maybe the man is really getting smaller."

(Sometimes I have a dream at night. That I am walking with grown-ups down the street where I have never been before. Suddenly they start to walk faster.
30 I have trouble keeping up because I am just small but

---

9 **blessed:** segensreich.
15 **to fib** (coll.): schwindeln.

170

they walk faster and faster. I don't run because I am embarrassed that I have to run when all they do is walk but they get real far ahead of me, farther away, they are smaller and smaller, and I am left behind. I
5 yell, "Wait for me, please," but they don't. They get smaller and smaller until they disappear. And I am alone.)

Just then Jessica started to run, but she tripped on the curb across the street and fell down. I got real mad
10 because you aren't supposed to run across the street, it isn't good safety. I went across and grabbed her on the arm and shook her. Sometimes my mom says she gets mad at me because she loves me and I never understood it before.

15 "You are supposed to obey the safety rules, Jessica," I said. "Like Officer Williams told us at assembly." (I am good at safety rules. Red means stop, green means go, and amber means caution. I don't know what yellow means.)

20 Jessica put her finger in her mouth and put one foot on top of her other like a little girl. She looked at me with her eyes, which are giants. She rocked back and forth and made her lips go like together. She looked at me.

25 "Take a picture, it lasts longer," I said.

She put her tongue on her lips and made them shiny.

"Your face is going to freeze like that," I said. She frowned more. She looked like she was going to cry again. Then she took her hand away from her mouth
30 and reached it out to me. She touched my arm.

---

9 **curb:** Bordstein(kante).
18 **amber:** bernsteinfarben; hier: dunkelorange.

"Got you last, ha ha!" she yelled, and skipped away down the street.

I caught her and shook her good.

"Don't tease me, Jessica," I said. "I hate it."

5 So she put her finger in her mouth again and looked like she was going to cry. I couldn't tell if she was acting or not. I couldn't tell with Jessica. I just looked at her on Seven Mile Road, and the cars drove by and the traffic was noisy all around us.

10 I heard another noise, it came from behind me. I turned around and there was a little kid on a bike, he had cards in his spokes and they made a loud noise. He drove reckless, man, he went up the curb and down into the street and almost got hit by cars and then up 15 the curb again. He had red sneakers. He passed us and I saw him go, his red sneakers went around and around on the pedals. Down Seven Mile he pulled his bike up on the back wheels and twirled around, and then disappeared.

20 Jessica and me walked to the big corner where Greenfield Road crosses Seven Mile, it was real noisy and had a lot of traffic that went fast.

"Let's cross", said Jessica, she was smiling now.

"No," I said. "We aren't allowed without a grown-25 up. My mom said never cross Seven Mile Road without a grown-up or I will get run over."

"Oh let's anyway," said Jessica, and she started to cross. The traffic was coming, I ran after her and pulled her back on the curb. I was shaking. I let go of her and

---

1 **got you last!:** hab ich dich endlich erwischt!

4 **to tease:** reizen, ärgern.

13 **reckless:** *recklessly* (adv.): rücksichtslos, unachtsam.

put my hands in my pockets. She just looked at me. Then she walked away.

"Jessica," I said, but she walked away. I thought, She is leaving now, she is mad at me because I didn't cross Seven Mile and I am chicken.

So I did something. I stepped off the curb into the street and started to cross. The cars screeched their brakes and somebody rolled down his window and yelled at me, but I kept going, and then I closed my eyes I was so scared but I kept crossing until I was on the other side of Seven Mile Road. When I looked though, Jessica wasn't even watching. She was talking to a man in front of the barber shop. Then she took his hand and he crossed her across Seven Mile Road and then went back himself. Jessica came up to me.

"You aren't supposed to cross by yourself, Burt," she said. "I was scared for you."

I just walked away. I almost cried, and then she ran after me but I didn't turn around because I was almost crying.

"I'm sorry Burt," she said. "I didn't mean you should cross."

I didn't talk for a few minutes but then I told her it was ok, and we went back up Seven Mile together again, but I looked at her, and I didn't know what she meant when she said things.

We came to Kiddyland. It is a lot next to the store that sells women's underpants (they have it in the window, it makes me embarrassed) and it has rides. But it was closed for the winter. There was a man

---

7 f. **to screech one's brakes:** mit Quietschen bremsen.
27 **lot:** Gelände.

though, he was taking the rides apart. He was dirty, he had a plaid shirt and a beard from not shaving.

Jessica stopped and leaned on the fence in front of Kiddyland and watched the man, he was unplugging
5 wires.

The man saw us. He started to walk to us and I ran away, but Jessica just stayed leaning on the fence.

"Aren't you kids supposed to be in school?" said the man. I saw he had dirt under his fingernails.

10 "It's a special holiday," said Jessica. "For us. Just for two children. Us."

The man smiled. "Oh yeah," he said. "I know that holiday. I used to observe it once in a while, that holiday."

15 Jessica smiled back at him but I wanted to go, you aren't supposed to talk to strangers.

"You kids want to ride the boat once before I take it down?" he said.

"No," I said.

20 "Yes," said Jessica.

I shook my head but she put her hand on me and looked at me. I said, "Jessica, it's wrong, Kiddyland is closed," but she smiled at me and pulled me and we went in.

25 The man was unplugging more wires. He picked me up and put me in a boat and he picked up Jessica and put her in a boat.

"Yep, after today this'll all be gone. Tomorrow there won't be any more Kiddyland. After tonight you two won't be able to come back to Kiddyland."

---

1 **to take s.th. apart:** etwas auseinander bauen, zerlegen, abbauen.

2 **plaid shirt:** Hemd mit Karomuster.

13 **to observe a holiday:** einen Feiertag begehen, einhalten.

"Not ever?" said Jessica. The man just smiled. He pulled a stick and the boats went around. We sat in them and went around. I pretended mine was real. You could put your hand in the water when you went
5 around and it made waves in it, it was cold. I rang the bell on mine and turned the steering wheel. And then something happened.

I turned around to see Jessica in her boat, but she wasn't there, it was empty, then I turned the other way
10 and I saw her. She was standing in the water in the middle of the boats, it was up to her legs, she had her finger in her mouth, she was crying.

I stood up in my boat and grabbed her arm and pulled her and she got into my boat. She was all wet. It
15 was freezing. She was crying. She sat next to me. I couldn't see the man. We went around and around.

Finally the man came back, only this time he was like mean. He picked us up out of the boats and pushed us out of Kiddyland.
20 "No more Kiddyland for you two," he kept saying over and over. It scared me.

Jessica was shivering again and we walked up Seven Mile. It was rainy still and there was wind too. I knew I had to save her. Then I saw something. It was Hanley-
25 Dawson Chevrolet, it is a car store on Seven Mile Road right near Kiddyland. It is a big room with glass walls where they have cars for sale. And on the window it had a big sign: COME SEE OUR NEW MODELS – FREE COFFEE AND DONUTS!
30 I took Jessica by the sleeve and pulled her into Hanley-Dawson Chevrolet.

6 **steering wheel:** Lenkrad.

It was warm inside, they had a couch for sitting and
Jessica sat on it. It was green. Then I went to the little
table where they had the coffee and donuts. There was
grown-ups all around, I had to stand in line. Hanley-
5 Dawson Chevrolet had desks with men in suits at them
and telephones and there was a lady with earplugs
in her ears who plugged in wires when the phones
rang. I waited in line like a little gentleman until it was
my turn and then I made Little Boys' Coffee for Jessi-
10 ca and I got a dirty look for using up all the milk. I
took her a donut too, it was blank, no white stuff. I
showed her dunking, my dad taught me. I dunk tuna
fish sandwiches in chocolate milk, it is delicious and
nutritious.
15 "Morty Nemsick calls this a sofa but my parents say
couch. What do you say, Jessica?" I talked to her. It
was talking to make her stop shivering. But she didn't
say anything. She held the coffee up to her mouth but
it started to spill all over because she was still shaking,
20 so I took it away and held it for her while she drank.
A man in a suit came up to us.
"Do you belong to someone?" he asked us.
"Yes, mister," I said.
He looked at our coats. "We're holding them for our
25 parents," I said. "They are elsewhere."
He walked away and I watched him go up to another man in a suit and look back at us and point. So I
got up. In front of us was a red car. There was a lady
and a man looking at it, they were dressed up, they
30 were younger than my parents, the lady had boots with

---

6 **earplug:** Ohrenstöpsel.
11 **blank:** hier: ohne Zuckerguss.

high heels on, she wore make-up. So I went and stood
like behind them.

"I think that interior is abysmal," said the lady. I
looked at her and nodded my head.

5 "It's optional," said the man.

I said, "Fabulous."

They both looked at me, so I waved. They looked at
my coat. "I have to grow into it," I said. "Very sensible
for winter."

10 The man in the suit watched me with the other man.
I waved at them too. The man and the lady walked
around the red car and I followed them, nodding when
they said something.

But then I looked at Jessica and she was shivering
15 even more, so I went to her. I had an idea.

"Come on," I said. I made her get up. I walked her
over to a big black car they had. The door was open. It
was black inside. It had big seats. It had windows. And
it was warm. We got in. We closed the doors. I sat in
20 the driver's side like the daddy and Jessica was next to
me. She took off her shoes and put blankee on her legs
and soon she started to be warm, I could tell.

I looked out the window. I did something I do frequent in cars. I looked out the window and found a
25 speck of dirt on it and then I closed one eye and went
up and down with my head and made it jump over
trees.

"All right, you kids get out of there. This isn't a toy

---

3 **interior:** Innenraum.
   abysmal: grässlich, abscheulich.
5 **to be optional:** zur Sonderausstattung gehören, wahlweise zur Verfü-
   gung stehen.

store," said the man in the suit. He stood outside the car. We locked the doors.

The man with the suit went and got the other man with a suit, who was older.

5 "That's it, kids," he said. "Out. Right now."

I ignored him. I gave him the silent treatment. He banged on the window with his fist and looked at the other man in a suit and said, "You get them out of here, you hear me?" and he went away. The other man
10 stayed and frowned at us.

Jessica put her face on blankee and hugged him. Her knees went up and down up and down, they had knee socks folded on top, which were smooth and like clear from being wet. I reached out my hand. I almost
15 touched them but I didn't. I put it on the seat instead.

Soon all the people at Hanley-Dawson Chevrolet were standing around the car looking at Jessica and me. I waved to them. It was like we were in a parade, only Jessica didn't look at them. She looked down just.
20 The man in the suit went and got the lady with the earplugs.

"You're a mother," he said. "See if you can do something with them."

The lady made a big smile and looked at us and said,
25 "Come now, children, don't you think it's about time you got home? I think your mommies and daddies must be worried about you."

But I was busy driving. I was on my way to Miami.

Jessica had ribbons in her hair that matched her
30 dress. They were wet though, from the rain outside,

---

6 **I gave him the silent treatment** (coll.): ich strafte ihn mit Schweigen und Nichtbeachtung.

and they dangled. And I went to touch one but I didn't.

One of the men in a suit started laughing and the other one said, "Don't encourage them."

Then the old one came out again. He yelled, "Where the hell is the key to that car? Doesn't anybody know what's going on here anymore?" Three men in suits went to find the key.

I kept driving to Florida and Jessica bent her head down and closed her eyes. When she bent down blankee slipped off her legs. I reached down to fix him, and when I did my hand hit something. Next to the steering wheel. It jingled. I looked. It was the keys to the car.

Then I did something. I didn't know how but I did. I reached down with my legs onto the long pedal and pushed it up and down up and down, and then I turned the key. Smoke came out, it made me jump, it was real loud. All the people ran back away from the car and the old man in the suit ran up and banged on the windows again with his fists.

"I'm going to call the police on you brats!" he said.

Then I didn't do anything, because I didn't know what was going to happen. But something happened. Jessica started talking.

"Raggedy Ann didn't die, Burt. I killed her in the hospital. I went to see Daddy. They took him in an ambulance. I was with my aunt, she took me into the room. My mom was in there, next to him, he was under a plastic thing, a tent, and he had tubes all in him. But his eyes were open. I walked up to him.

---

1 **to dangle:** baumeln.

'Daddy, it's me, Contessa,' I said, but he didn't say anything. 'It's me, Contessa,' I said. He looked right at me but he didn't say anything. He acted like he didn't even know who I was. I said, 'It's me, Daddy, it's me,' but he looked the other way and I thought it was the plastic, why he couldn't see, so I reached to pull it away from him but my mom grabbed my hand and I pushed her away. I was mad at Daddy, he wouldn't even talk to me, I yelled at him. I screamed that he was being mean and wouldn't talk to me. My aunt pulled me away, out of the room. She made me sit outside, on plastic chairs that were hard. I had Raggedy Ann with me.

Then my mom came out of the room and she was crying. She told my aunt it was all over and to take me home. But I screamed that I wanted to see Daddy. My aunt held me real hard, she wouldn't let me. She said that there are some things children don't understand.

And then I decided that I wasn't going to be children anymore. I took Raggedy Ann and killed her in the wastebasket by the elevator."

And Jessica started to cry. She cried and cried in the car, all bent over and I didn't know what to do. So I put my arms out, like my dad does when I have nightmares, and I put them on Jessica, I put them around Jessica and she leaned on me, on my front. I hugged her in the car. I hugged her very tight, while grown-ups pounded on the windows all around us.

19

The policeman had a gun but he didn't kill us. He was
nice as a policeman and liked children, but said it was
dangerous to drive cars inside a store. He called Jessica's mother on the telephone but she wasn't home and
then he called my house but Jeffrey answered and said
it was the wrong number. So the policeman said we
could go if we promised to go straight home, and when
we left I heard the old man in a suit say, "Is that all,
you're letting them go just like that?" and the policeman said, "Weren't you ever a kid, mister?"

The sky was just gorgeous, which is what my mom
says when I come home dirty, it was gray like dirt and
drizzling. The streets were shiny from the water and
you could see your breath. We walked back.

I followed Jessica to watch her. We passed Maxwell's on the other side coming back. The big clock
outside the bank said four o'clock.

We didn't talk anymore. We were silence all the way
back to Jessica's house. In the driveway were two cars,
a station wagon and a little one, in black. I knew the
little one was Jessica's father's car. Jessica opened the
side door of the house and went in but I didn't want to.
I waited outside until she said to come in. I went in.

The lights were all off, nobody was home, no pets

---

12 **gorgeous:** prachtvoll, herrlich.
21 **station wagon:** Kombi(wagen).

even. Jessica took off my mom's coat and hung it up
but I left mine on. Someone was in the pocket, Monkey Cuddles, he was sleeping. Jessica went through the
hall to the living room. She didn't talk. She sat down
5 on the sofa sideways and put her feet on it which made
dark spots where they got it wet. (But you shouldn't
put your feet on the furniture, it ruins it, said my mom,
and you have to give it away. Once my grandfather
sold all the chairs in our house without telling anyone.
10 A man came and was loading them in a truck when my
mom got home. She yelled at the man. She said, "What
can you say about an eighty-year-old man who doesn't
know the value of furniture?")

I stood in the hall and looked at Jessica. In the
15 corner of the living room was a grandfather's clock.
Captain Kangaroo has one that dances, but Jessica's
didn't, he didn't even have the face, just a thing on the
bottom that went back and forth back and forth.

Next to the sofa was a table with doilies, which are
20 cloth snowflakes, and coasters. (I enjoy coasters as
items, you don't have to wind them.) Jessica looked
out the window behind her and bounced one foot up
and down up and down.

Outside was Mr Moon. In Music we had a song,

25   O Mr Moon, Moon
       Bright and Silvery Moon
       Won't you please shine down on me.

---

15 **grandfather's clock:** Standuhr.
19 **doily:** Zier-, Spitzendeckchen.
20 **coaster: 1.** Untersetzer; **2.** Rodelschlitten (AE).
26 **silvery:** silbrig glänzend.

182

O Mr Moon, Moon
Bright and Silvery Moon
I'm as blue as I can be.

I'm going to shoot that possum
Fore he starts to run
Going to shoot that possum
With my possum gun.

Oh Mr Moon, Moon
Bright and Silvery Moon
Won't you please shine down on me.

"Do you see the Man in the Moon?" I said. The
clouds went over the moon and made it go on and off.
And once I was standing on my front porch looking at
the moon and my mom came out and tried to show me
the Man in the Moon, but I couldn't see him. I have
never been able to see him.

Jessica didn't say anything. I sat down on the sofa.
Outside the rain stopped. On the edge of the sky it was
red. Everything in the house was brown. In winter it
gets dark early and you turn the clocks backwards. The
sky is where God lives, I have prayed to him there. I
prayed for Jessica's father to not be dead, but God
didn't help me. When I was little I used to think that
night was when clouds covered the sky.

"You got the sofa wet," I told Jessica. She looked at
me and said, "When my daddy died my mom covered
everything with sheets so the company wouldn't spill

---

4 **possum:** Opossum (amerikanische Beutelratte).
5 **fore** (coll.): *before.*
20 **to turn the clock backwards:** die Uhr zurückstellen.

on it. She only uncovered it yesterday. She said it was time to stop being sad, but she cried all night." Jessica looked at where it was wet. "She should have left it on."

I looked out the window, and put my nose on it and breathed out donuts. I said, "Look, Jessica, donuts," but she was looking at something else, by the stairs, hanging on the bannister, a purse.

Across the street a porch light went on. It got darker outside. I looked for the moon but it was gone now. A dog went down the sidewalk, a man walked him. An airplane went over, the noise was behind it. Down the block somebody yelled, "I've got to move the car," and Jessica stood up and walked into the hall, she looked at the purse, and said, "That's my mother's purse." Then she looked up the stairs. Then she walked up the stairs.

I sat on the sofa. There was a candle on the table on the doily but it wasn't lit, it was off. The refrigerator in the kitchen hummed. The grandfather's clock rang five times. And outside the sky turned dark blue with no stars. I folded my hands up in my lap and waited, but Jessica didn't come back down.

I got up. I walked into the hall. It smelled like Jessica. I looked at the purse.

I listened. There wasn't any noise. I put my foot on the first step. It had carpet on it. I was standing on the stairs.

I walked up the stairs. When I got to the top I looked around. I could hardly see. I waited for my eyes

---

8 **bannister:** Geländer.

to get used to it. There was a bathroom. Next to it was a bedroom with a big bed for two people. Next to it was a closet, I opened it and it had sheets and towels in it. Then I looked down the hall. At the end I saw another room, the door was open and Jessica was inside, sitting on her bed sideways looking out the window, her feet hung over the edge.

I walked up to her doorway and stopped. She didn't hear me. I stood and watched her just. Her face was lit up from outside and her eyes had diamonds in them. I waited and waited and soon she started to sing a little song.

> Kukaberra sits
> In the old gum tree
> Merry merry king
> Of the bush is he
> Laugh Kukaberra
> Laugh Kukaberra
> Gay your life must be.

I listened. I watched her lips open and close open and close. She leaned on three pillows. One was pink, one was checkered, one was plain. Her feet dangled over the side of the bed. I watched.

In the corner of the room was a wood horse that was really a chair. On her ceiling was a lamp with clowns on it, and hanging from her wall over her bed was Jerry the Puppet.

Jessica pushed off her shoes and they fell on the

22 **checkered:** kariert.
   plain: ungemustert, ohne Muster.

floor. She pulled her legs up on the bed, she had on
knee socks still, folded on top and smooth and soft.
Then she said something.

"Peter Pan is a girl." She was looking out the
5 window still. "They made her look like a boy but she is
a girl, they just cut her hair short and made her wear a
tight brassiere."

(I saw it too, on television, and it made me want to
fly so I made my dad call up the television station to
10 find out how they did it, but Jeffrey said there wasn't
anybody on the other end, that my dad lied to me.)

"I'm not old enough to wear a brassiere," said Jessica. "But I have one, my mom gave it to me, for when I
am."

15 She went into her closet and took it out. She showed
it to me, it made me feel funny. It was wrong. I'm not
supposed to look at them. But then I did something, I
took it and put it on myself, only backwards. "Look,
Jessica," I said. "I'm a camel."

20 It surprised me that she laughed. She laughed like I
never heard before, it was like singing. I put the brassiere on my head and jumped up and down and she
laughed more and I put it on my face and then she fell
on her bed laughing.

25 "Knock knock," I said (it was a joke).
"Who's there?"
"Boo."
"Boo who?" said Jessica.
"You don't have to cry about it," I said.
30 Jessica looked at me. "I'm not," she said.
"No, see. You don't have to cry about it."

---

7 **brassiere:** Büstenhalter.

"I'm not, Burt." She stopped laughing.

"No, it's a joke."

"What is?"

She just turned around to the window again, because she didn't understand.

"Jessica, it's a joke," I said.

But she wouldn't turn back around. I watched her back, it made little humps, she was crying.

"Jessica." I said her name but she just put her head down on the bed and her shoulders went up and down up and down. I didn't know what to do, so I walked next to the bed.

I tried to show her a magic trick, you pull your thumb off it looks like, but she wouldn't look.

"Maybe we can pretend, Jessica," I said. "Something. So you won't be sad."

"No," she said. "That's for children. I don't want to be children anymore." She said, "I hate it," and hit her bed, and said "I hate it" again and hit her bed, and again, she made noise with her voice like an animal. "I hate being children!" she screamed and put her head inside her arm and layed down on the bed and cried.

I didn't know what to do. I stood and watched and was angry. Because I am children too. And I hate it too.

My mom told me that someday when I was grown up I would love somebody and it would mean I would want to stop everyone from hurting her. I used to think it was Shrubs. But it wasn't. It was Jessica.

I sat down on the bed next to her and put my hand on her hair on the ribbons, and I pulled one of them,

---

8 **hump:** hier: Zucken, ruckartige Bewegung nach oben.

and it came undone and fell on the bed. And the other
one. I held it in my hand. And I put it on my cheek,
because it was softness. Like Jessica.

When she looked up at me her hair was in her face. I
pushed it back with my hands and it was wet too but
not from outside but from crying. I picked up a tear on
my finger and put it in my eyes.

I put my arms around Jessica like Daddy does when
I cry and did this to the back of her head. She rolled
over and leaned on me with her side on me, it was
warm. I took off my coat and someone fell out onto
the bed. Monkey Cuddles. I put him on the window sill
looking outside, to keep guard over Jessica Renton
and me.

And I looked at her crying and I said something real
soft. "I won't let anybody hurt you. I won't. I'll make it
so we won't be children anymore."

And she looked up at me with her eyes and pushed
down on me with her head on my stomach and I pulled
her to me tight and it was warm on me. Outside I saw
it started to snow and Monkey Cuddles watched it in
the wind but we were warm inside. And suddenly
something happened. I saw the streetlights go on. They
lit up and shined on us. Jessica put her face against my
stomach and said, "You are my friend," and her eyes
had diamonds in them.

I put my chin on her hair and she put her face up on
mine, it was soft as blankee and she put her mouth on
my face, she pulled on my shirt. She rolled over and
her dress went up over her arms that were around me

---

1 **to come undone:** sich lösen, abgehen.

and she went back on the bed and pulled me on top of her and I felt her hands in my pockets, they pushed down over my legs, over me. I felt an airplane under my tummy, with rubber bands that wound up tighter and tighter. Jessica held my tushy and made it go up and down up and down. In front of her, where I felt her, she had a little tushy on her, and it was soft like kissing. And suddenly I heard a noise, from very far away, coming to Jessica's house. Running down Seven Mile Road. Hooves. A horse running with nobody on it. Blacky. Louder and louder past all the stores. And then I heard something else. A bike with cards in the spokes, next to Blacky, coming, with nobody riding, racing louder and louder, to me. Under my tummy the airplane wound tighter and tighter and I held Jessica and her legs were around me and I said, "Don't be scared anymore," and she said, "I'm not now, I'm not now. I'm not now." The noise got louder and Blacky and the bike were nearer and I knew they were coming, the rubber band was tighter and I thought I was dying too, I was almost dead. And then I flew. I flew over the house and the street and Maxwell's, over Lauder and school, over everything, down to Jessica. I saw I was almost there. I was almost there. And then I was there.

Somebody screamed, "Oh my God." The lights went on. She pulled me off the bed and threw me against the wall and blood came out of my face. I slid to the floor. All I saw was her purse and she grabbed Jessica and I screamed, "Don't you touch her don't you touch her," and slammed her with my fists but she threw me down again and I couldn't stand up.

189

20

"What's your phone number!" screamed Jessica's
mother. I thought I couldn't move, my face had blood
on it. I felt like I had to throw up.

"What's the number, can't you understand English?" She grabbed my arm. "I'm talking to you!" I
closed my eyes and went away.

Jessica kneeled on her bed with her face in the pillows. She cried and cried. When her mother went to
touch her she wouldn't let her.

"How could this happen?" said her mother. "What
kind of disgusting animal are you anyway? You should
be locked up someplace. What kind of family could
you come from, to raise something like you. I'm going
to take care of you though, don't worry, you'll never
do this again, not to my little girl, or anyone. Do you
hear me?"

She grabbed my hair and pulled my face back.

"Do you hear me?"

I came back. I opened my eyes. "If you touch her," I
whispered, "I'll kill you."

I don't know how she got the number but she called
my parents. She said I said I would kill her.

My mom came and put me in the car. I tried to stay
with Jessica, I held on to her bed, I had a tantrum, but
I couldn't hold on. When I got home there was a policeman and my father. I didn't talk to anyone. My
mother put medicine on my face. She was crying I remember.

I remember they made me go to bed and the doctor came and gave me medicine to make me sleepy. I couldn't get up. I almost can't remember, but I remember the phone, it kept ringing like bells, and I heard it was Jessica's mother.

The next day my mother and father put me in the car and brought me here, to The Children's Trust Residence Center. And left me. Jessica's mother made them do it, but they said they thought it was best too.

And now I have been here for two months. Hanukah was three weeks ago. I got clothes in a box from my mom and dad, it was tied up with string. I took the string and tied it around one of my socks and hung it on the wall, like a puppet.

I don't write here frequent anymore, because Dr Nevele says it is better to talk to him at appointments. I don't even come to the Quiet Room frequent. I can control myself.

Rudyard left The Children's Trust Residence Center, but he came back. But I don't see him, he doesn't come to my wing or the Playroom, he is upstairs. I think about him when I go swimming. I can do the Dog Paddle. I am going to teach it to Monkey Cuddles when I get home. He likes swimming except I will never see him again. He was at Jessica's house. I think her mother killed him.

I saw Rudyard. It was upstairs where Mrs Cochrane took me to see another doctor who showed me pictures and had me name things. It was a test. When I came out Rudyard was in the hall with a child, he was holding it in his arms, it made faces.

23 **dog paddle** (coll.): (einfaches) Schwimmen nach Art des Hundes.

He looked at me. I looked at him. We looked at each other for a long time. Then he said, "I have something for you."

He put the child down and stood up. He looked at
5 me again and reached into his back pocket.

"I've been carrying this around for a week," he said. "I don't even know why. Tell Dr Nevele you found it somewhere."

I looked at it, it was an envelope. When I looked up
10 at Rudyard he was crying. He was crying for me. So I did something. I put my hand under my chin and gave him the High Sign.

The child ran down the hall and Rudyard ran after him. Down the hall, he got smaller and smaller.

15 I opened the envelope. Then I closed it. It was shaking in my hands. Because I was afraid.

That night I couldn't sleep. I layed in bed in my wing and looked at the ceiling, there was a window in it, where the lights shined in from the hall.

20 Outside the doors I heard the janitors go home, they said they were like to freeze their dicks off. And when they were gone there wasn't anybody. It was late. It was quiet. Manny sucked his thumb and Howie breathed in bed next to me. I just watched the window
25 in the ceiling, and watched and watched.

I got out of bed. I reached under my pillow and took the letter, Jessica's letter. I went to the door. I looked out. It was empty. I went. I walked next to the wall. It had somebody on it, my shadow. We walked next to
30 the wall, me and me.

21 **to freeze one's dick off** (vulg.): sich den Schwanz abfrieren.

192

I was going somewhere with myself.

I went through a door that said stairs. It was stairs. I went up them and up them. My feet made echoes but I didn't stop. Then I went out another door and turned this way. I went all the way to the end and then I turned this way. I went through glass doors and then I was in another hall. There was a nurse behind a table. She read a book. She didn't see me. Then I went through another door. Inside the room was a row of beds. I walked down the row to the last bed.

Carl was tied down, they had straps on him. He didn't even try to move even, but he saw me with his eyes. They were open. He couldn't sleep either. There was a folding chair by the window. I took it and opened it and sat down next to Carl's bed. He smiled at me. I wasn't afraid.

"It's me," I said. "From the Playroom, remember I pushed you."

Carl didn't say anything. His eyes went sideways in his head once but he looked at me.

"I am confused," I said, "about Rudyard and Dr Nevele. Rudyard showed me swimming and he was my friend, but he lied about the wall, about reading the wall."

Carl smiled. I saw his stomach go up and down up and down. Noise came from the other beds, it sounded like puppies. It was children.

"And Dr Nevele. He doesn't understand children and it makes him sad. He said I didn't have any letters."

Carl stopped moving.

14 **folding chair:** Klappstuhl.

193

"And now there isn't anybody. I wish I was home. I wish I wasn't anywhere."

I sat with Carl for the rest of the night. I just sat next to him and he watched me, smiling, and I stayed. It was very quiet in the room, like everyone had gone away to heaven.

When morning came I went. I walked back down the hall. Nurses came in and took their coats off and hung them. I went to the Quiet Room. I opened the door and turned on the light, but someone was in there, curled up on the floor against the wall.

She woke up when I came in and sat up and looked at me and rubbed her eyes and she looked like a little baby almost. She put on her glasses to see who it was, and it was me.

"Mrs Cochrane."

She had wrinkles from the floor. She was like dizzy. She took her glasses off and rubbed her eyes. She started to get up but she couldn't. She was too old. I looked at her, she was like a little child. I knew she came there to wait for me because I wasn't in my bed, she had checked on me. I watched her. She didn't say anything. Sat just, on the floor in front of the wall, where she had wrote *He wanted to see time fly.* I knew it was her.

I was very sleepy. I turned off the light in the Quiet Room and layed down on the floor next to her and she put her arm on me. I moved closer and she kept her arm on me. She kept it there while I slept.

---

17 **wrinkle:** Runzel, Falte.
   dizzy: schwindlig; benommen, schlaftrunken.

21

Dear Randy,

I don't know if I'll be able to write very soon again because my mother is taking me to private school tomorrow. It is far, in Ohio. She said there are lots of nice children there, I will forget.

The doctor at the hospital told her to send me. He said that what happened will bother me for a long time, and maybe I'll have bad dreams. He gave my mother pills to give me to sleep.

The night I got home from the hospital she put me to bed in her room and gave me a pill. But I hid it in my mouth and spit it out. And when she was gone I got up and went into my own room. I got in bed but I couldn't sleep. I was afraid. Then I heard a noise, it scared me and I turned on the lamp. Then it went away. But when I turned the light off it came again. I was scared. I listened real hard.

It was dark, there was only a little light that came in from the streetlights. And I saw Monkey Cuddles sitting on the window looking out where you put him. It was him. He was singing

> Kukaberra sits
> In the old gum tree
> Merry merry king
> Of the bush is he
> Laugh Kukaberra

---

8 **to bother s.o.:** jdm. zu schaffen machen.

Laugh Kukaberra
Gay your life must be.

I listened to him sing it over and over. It was soft. And
when I fell asleep I dreamed about rainbows.

Jessica

Dear Jessica,

Once I was five. It was summer. I got to stay up late because there wasn't school. And one night I had a bad
dream.

I woke up. It was all dark in my room. There was a
shadow over the closet. Everything was quiet. I didn't
feel good. I was sweating. It was cold on me. I sat up and
waited. I waited and waited. Then I got out of bed. I
pointed at the door and went. I walked into the hall in
my pajamas. I stood in the hall next to the night-light in
front of my parents' room. I listened. But I didn't hear
anything. Inside of their room was black.

I stood in my pajamas. I looked in my parents' room
but it was dark. I listened but I didn't hear any noise.
And I said something, very soft, in the hall.

Is anybody there?

BURT

---

15 **night-light:** Nachtbeleuchtung, -licht.

Editorische Notiz

Der englische Text folgt der Ausgabe: Howard Buten, *When I Was Five I Killed Myself*, Woodstock / New York: The Overlook Press, 2000. Das Glossar erklärt in der Regel alle Wörter, die nicht in *Reclams Englischem Wörterbuch* von Dieter Hamblock (Stuttgart: Reclam, 1996) verzeichnet sind.

Im Glossar verwendete Abkürzungen

adv.	adverb
AE	American English
arch.	archaic (veraltet)
coll.	colloquial (umgangssprachlich)
fig.	figuratively (übertragen)
Fr.	French
Ital.	Italian
Lat.	Latin
o.s.	oneself
pej.	pejorative (abschätzig)
pl.	plural
s.o.	someone
Span.	Spanish
s.th.	something
vulg.	vulgar (vulgär, derb)
Yidd.	Yiddish

Literaturhinweise

Ausgaben

Burt, New York: Holt, Rinehart & Winston, 1981.

Quand j'avais cinq ans je m'ai tué, übers. von Jean-Pierre Carasso, Paris: Seuil, 1981.

When I Was Five I Killed Myself, Woodstock / New York: The Overlook Press, 2000.

Monsieur Butterfly, Paris: Seuil, 1987. [Unveröff. engl. Originalmanuskript u. d. T. *Mister Butterfly*, 1980.]

Le Coeur sous le Rouleau Compresseur, Paris: Seuil, 1984.

Il faudra bien te couvrir, Paris: Seuil, 1989. [Unveröff. engl. Originalmanuskript u. d. T. *What to my Wandering Eyes*, 1989.]

(zus. mit Jean-Pierre Carasso), *Histoire de Rofo, Clown*, Paris: Éditions de l'Olivier, 1991.

C'était mieux avant, Paris: Éditions de l'Olivier, 1993. [Engl. Arbeitstitel: *I Understand that If Not Completely Satisfied I Will Be Issued a Full Refund.*]

Ces enfants qui ne viennent pas d'une autre planète, les autistes, mit Illustrationen von Woszniak, Paris: Gallimard, 1994.

Quand est-ce qu'on arrive?, Paris: Éditions de l'Olivier, 2000. [Engl. Arbeitstitel: *The Queen of »Are we almost there«?.*]

Burt, übers. von Christiane Buchner, Hamburg: Kellner, 1992.

Burt, übers. von Christiane Buchner, Hamburg: Rogner & Bernhard bei Zweitausendundeins, 1994.

Burt, übers. von Christiane Buchner, München: Goldmann, 1997 (btb, Nr. 72110).

Sekundärliteratur

Anon., »Entretien avec ... Howard Buten. Coursive«. http://www.sanvnf.fr/fr/press/cours/c00/cours0005.htm

Anon., »Howard Buten: Burt«. [Rezension zur Taschenbuchausgabe bei Goldmann, btb Nr. 72110.] www.skult.de/titel/buch/burt

Ebel, Sabine, »Ein Happy-End als Anfang vom Ende. Über den Roman *Ohne Rücksicht auf Verluste* von Howard Buten, Psychiater, Schriftsteller und Clown«, in: *Berliner Zeitung*, 11. Februar 1995.

Fasca, Chad, »The Quiet Room. Room without a View on Adolescence«. www.actorsupdate.com/review102400.html

Garza, David, »*When I Was Five I Killed Myself*«. [Rezension.] www.auschron.com/issues/dispatch/2000-09-08/books_bookshelf.html

Guttman, Cynthia, »*Monsieur Butterfly* and Autistic Children«, in: *International Herald Tribune*, 8. Juni 1987.

Johnson, Marguerite, »The Unknown American«, in: *Time* 143 (18. April 1994) Nr. 16.

Joyce, Cynthia, »*When I Was Five I Killed Myself*«, in: *New York Times*, 30. Juli 2000. [Rezension.]

Péan, Stanley, »Howard Buten: En trois dimensions«. [Interview]. www.librairiepantoute.qc.ca/magazine/articles/buten.asp

Silber, Martine, »Le cœur en pièces détachées«, in: *Le Monde*, 1. März 2001. [Rezension von *Quand j'avais cinq ans je m'ai tué* und *Quand est-ce qu'on arrive?*.]

Nachwort

Howard Buten wird 1950 in Detroit (Michigan) als Sohn einer ehemaligen Sängerin und Tänzerin sowie eines Rechtsanwalts geboren. Schon früh fällt der Junge durch vielseitige intellektuelle und musische Begabungen auf. Im zarten Alter von acht Jahren übernimmt er bereits Solorollen im Schulchor seiner Grundschule und bringt sich selbst Bauchrednerei bei. In den darauf folgenden Jahren beginnt er, Geige, Trompete und Schlagzeug zu spielen. Während seiner ganzen Schulzeit an der *high school* spielt er in Bands und mit sechzehn schreibt er Orchestrierungen für die Jazzcombo seiner Schule. Mit Karikaturen für Kunstausstellungen verdient er sich ein Zubrot.

Auch auf literarischem Gebiet ist Buten ein Frühstarter. Mit elf Jahren verfasst er *David and the Cubs* – die Geschichte zweier Freunde im Widerstand gegen Hitler –, findet allerdings keinen Verleger, was er aus kindlicher Sicht mit gespieltem Erstaunen humorvoll kommentiert: »I wrote my first novel when I was eleven. It was a war epic about the German resistance during the rise of the Third Reich, a saga of two friends torn apart by the horrors of war and conflicting ideologies. [...] (A scandal! No one would publish my novel! What did they mean, it had to be typed?)« (S. 3). Mit zwölf Jahren gewinnt er einen Gedichtwettbewerb und nach einer langen Reihe von Absagen kommt 1981 schließlich sein vierter Romanvorschlag, *Burt*, bei Holt, Rinehart & Winston, New York, heraus.

Neben seinen literarischen Ambitionen ist es früh Butens Lebensziel, Arzt zu werden. Bereits mit zwölf Jahren macht er naturwissenschaftliche Versuche in einem eigens im Untergeschoss des elterlichen Hauses eingerichteten Labor und gründet mit vier Freunden den »Future Scientists' Club.« 1964 beginnt er als Freiwilliger mit Muskelschwundpatienten zu arbeiten und leistet ein Praktikum im Sinai Hospital in Detroit ab. In den Jahren darauf engagiert er sich bei der Behandlung und Förderung von Lernbehinderten und Lernschwachen.

Das Jahr 1974 bedeutet eine Weichenstellung für Butens künftiges Engagement als Arzt. In seiner Freiwilligenzeit am Children's Orthogenic Center in Detroit und am UCLA Neuropsychiatric Hospital in Westwood versucht er, in die Gedanken- und Gefühlswelt autistischer Kinder und junger Erwachsener vorzudringen, deren Verhaltensmuster zu ergründen und über mögliche Therapieformen zu reflektieren.[1]

1981 beginnt Buten ein Studium am Fielding Institute im kalifornischen Santa Barbara, das er mit dem Doktorgrad in klinischer Psychologie abschließt. In seiner Doktorarbeit befasst er sich mit dem Thema der Empathie gegenüber dem Patienten als einer Grundvoraussetzung für einen Therapieerfolg. Im Zuge des riesigen Echos auf seinen Erstling mit Millionenauflage in Frankreich[2] bekommt Buten ein Angebot als klinischer Psychiater in der Pariser Spezialklinik für Autismus Barthélémy Durand. Er siedelt nach Paris über. Nach zweijähriger Praxis und weiteren Erfahrungen mit erwachsenen Autisten im Klinikum Perry-Vaucluse eröffnet Buten 1989 das Centre Koschise in St. Michel-sur-Orge[3] als Pilotprojekt für das Centre Adam-Shelton (1997) in Paris-St.Denis, das er nach seinem ersten autistischen Patienten in den Staaten benennt und das auf schwere Formen von Autismus und Kinderpsychosen spezialisiert ist.

Neben Literatur und klinischer Tätigkeit in der Psychiatrie findet Buten seit 1973 Erfüllung als Clown Buffo. Inspiriert vom genialen und gefeierten Schweizer Musikclown Grock, erobert er seither die Herzen seiner jugendlichen und erwachsenen Zuschauer in aller Welt. Für seine originellen und ein-

---

1 »I took the Yellow Pages, opened them to ›R‹ for Retarded and went along to the local mental institution and offered myself as a volunteer. I fell in love with the kids, I spent all my time there, and then, after a year and a half, they let me try out some of my own ideas.« Zit. nach: Cynthia Guttman, »*Monsieur Butterfly* and Autistic Children«, in: *International Herald Tribune*, 8. Juni 1987, S. 1.

2 Erschienen unter dem Titel *Quand j'avais cinq ans je m'ai tué*, übers. von Jean-Pierre Carasso (Paris: Seuil, 1981).

3 Zu den Zielen des Centre Koschise und des Centre Adam-Shelton vgl. http://www.arrowbase.net/adamshelton/origines.htm

fallsreichen Darbietungen auf französischen Bühnen erhielt er 1998 den Prix Molière für den besten Soloauftritt.

Butens Clown Buffo lebt nicht von der platten Komik des Hanswursts oder von wohlfeilen Slapstickeinlagen. Er will kein Verschnitt von Charlie Chaplin sein. Wie Buster Keaton ist Buffo stumm, kann dafür aber Trompete, Cello, Violine, Schlagzeug und Klavier spielen. »It's all emotion [...]. You really have to make people believe you are surprised or sad, that a trumpet is really coming out of your pants or balloons out of your mouth.«[4]

In vielen Fernseh- und Theaterauftritten rührte Buffos stumme, aber vielsagende und suggestive Komik vor allem französische Fans zu Tränen oder brachte sie zu unbändigem Lachen. So agierte Buten beispielsweise im renommierten Pariser Olympia oder im Théâtre Tintamarre ebenso wie zusammen mit dem Geiger Pierre Amoyal auf verschiedenen Schweizer Bühnen. Zum Zeichen der künstlerischen Wertschätzung Butens wurde ihm 1991 die höchste literarische Auszeichnung in Frankreich, die Würde eines *Chevalier des Arts et Lettres*, verliehen. Buten lebt heute abwechselnd in Paris und New York.

Die Rezeptionsgeschichte von *Burt* (1981) alias *When I Was Five I Killed Myself* (2000) verlief mit erheblichen Brüchen. Das Werk kam zunächst in Kleinauflage heraus und wurde gegen Butens Überzeugung als Jugendbuch vermarktet, was seiner Meinung nach ein Hemmschuh für den ganz großen Erfolg in Amerika war. Es wurde in der Folgezeit kaum nachgefragt und war bald ohne Aussicht auf eine Neuauflage vergriffen. Eine Erklärung für den Misserfolg liefert der Autor selbst: »[American] editors didn't believe many people would be interested in reading about a sensitive child unfairly placed in a mental institution.«[5] Ganz anders, nämlich mit überschäumender Euphorie, wurde das Werk in Frankreich aufgenom-

4 Zit. nach: Guttman, 1987, S. 1.
5 Zit. nach: Marguerite Johnson, »The Unknow American«, in: *Time*, 18. April 1994.

men, wo es heute Millionenbestseller ist und bereits als Klassiker gilt: »*Burt* wound up being published in France, in French, under its present title. It became a cult bestseller, a sort of French *Catcher in the Rye*« (S. 4). Daneben liegen von dem Werk Übersetzungen ins Deutsche, Italienische, Schwedische und Dänische vor.

Die Breitenwirkung von Butens Erstling in Frankreich kann auch heute gar nicht hoch genug eingeschätzt werden. Jean-Claude Sussfeld nahm den Romanstoff als Vorlage für seinen gleichnamigen Film von 1993, mit Dimitri Rougeul und Salomé Lelouch in den beiden Kinderhauptrollen.[6] In Amerika wurde das Werk immerhin mehrfach zu Bühnenfassungen umgearbeitet.[7] Der durchschlagende Erfolg in Frankreich veranlasste Buten dazu, mit *Le Coeur sous le Rouleau compresseur* 1984 (dt. *Ohne Rücksicht auf Verluste*, Hamburg: Kellner, 1994 [vergriffen]) eine Art Fortsetzung zu schreiben. Ein weiterer Roman, in den ebenfalls seine Erfahrung als Kinderpsychologe einfließt, trägt den Titel *Monsieur Butterfly* (1987). Sein derzeit letzter Roman *Quand est-ce qu'on arrive?* erschien 2000, bezeichnenderweise wieder in Frankreich (vgl. Literaturhinweise S. 199).

Der achtjährige Burton Rembrandt, kurz Burt genannt, ist Hauptfigur und Ich-Erzähler der vorliegenden Geschichte: aus jüdischer Familie, Grundschüler im zweiten Jahr, frühreif, vielseitig begabt. Burt ist gut in Zeichnen, im Singen, in Buchstabieren und Rechtschreibung und außerdem ein geschickter Bastler, der im Nu die Marionette Jerry the Puppet zusammenfügt (S. 141 f.). So gibt es zunächst nur angedeutete Gründe, warum er sich in einem Heim für schwer verhaltensgestörte und geistig behinderte Kinder und Jugendliche befindet: »I am here for what I did to Jessica« (S. 9). Diese Verfehlung – der vollzogene Geschlechtsakt mit einer Mitschülerin – beschäftigt Burt bis in seine zahlreichen Angstträume hinein

---

/ 6 Vgl. http://www.cinemaot.multimania.com/video073.html.
7 Vgl. etwa *The Quiet Room* von Lucie Tiberghien am Directors Company Theatre in New York und *Burt* von Teddy Yaeger, produziert von Elastic Productions und aufgeführt beim Fringe Theatre Festival 2001.

(»Then Jessica turned around and looked at me, and said, ›Why did you do that to me, Burt, what you did?‹«, S. 38), wie er überhaupt von panischen Ängsten, die bis zu Verfolgungswahn und Realitätsverlust führen, heimgesucht wird.[8] So hält er einen harmlosen Wasserstandableser (S. 164) oder einen Lieferanten von Maxwell's (S. 168) für »truant officers«, deren Aufgabe es ist, Schulschwänzer dingfest zu machen.

Seine übersteigerte Sensibilität und angstbesetzte Beeindruckbarkeit manifestieren sich bereits im Eingangskapitel. Burt empfindet die Tagesnachrichten im Fernsehen überwiegend als bedrohlich und schwer zu verkraften. Auf den sinnlosen Unfalltod eines Mädchens, über den im Fernsehen berichtet wird, reagiert er als Fünfjähriger mit (symbolischem) Selbstmord, zum Zeichen des Protestes gegen eine feindselige, grausame und ungerechte Welt (S. 8; vgl. auch Buchtitel).

Burts Lebens- und Leidensgeschichte, die in den späten fünfziger Jahren des 20. Jahrhunderts anzusiedeln ist, erschließt sich dem Leser nach und nach in einundzwanzig Kapiteln, die teils den Behandlungsalltag im Heim (Kap. 2,5,7,12 und, zum Teil, 14 und 20 sowie Kap. 21) mit dem euphemistischen Namen Children's Trust Residence Center, teils in Rückblenden sein seitheriges Leben widerspiegeln. Der kleine Patient lehnt jegliche verbale Kommunikation mit dem verantwortlichen klinischen Psychiater, Dr. Nevele, ab: »Dr Nevele [...] I will never talk to you« (S. 104). Den Grund für diese Verhaltensweise liefert eine Schlüsselszene, in der Nevele seinen Patienten mit etwas gezwungenem Humor auffordert: »Won't you step into my chambers?« (S. 52). Diese an sich harmlos gemeinte Formulierung weckt in Burt grausame Filmerinnerungen an die Folterkammer eines gewissen Dr. Night. Von Burts jüdischem Hintergrund her spielt möglicherweise die vage Vorstellung von Euthanasieärzten und Gaskammern ebenfalls eine Rolle. Fortan widersetzt sich Burt

8 »I am scared of going to bed, because there are monsters in my closet« (S. 28); »I am afraid of the news« (S. 7); »I am scared of pins« (S. 22); »I was scared« (S. 36); »We went to the snakes who stuck their tongues out and I got scared« (S. 75); vgl. auch sein Bettnässen (S. 132).

Neveles Behandlungsversuchen rabiat, kratzt, beißt und wirft sich auf den Boden. Diese »tantrums« (S. 28) oder »conniption fits« (S. 24) sind bei ihm eine eingeschliffene und häufig praktizierte Form des Widerstands, die ihre Wirkung in der Regel bei Erwachsenen nicht verfehlt. Der Psychiater muss erkennen, dass ein Vertrauensverhältnis zu seinem neuen Patienten unmöglich ist. Deshalb lässt er zu, dass dieser seine Lebensgeschichte an die Wand des »Beruhigungszimmers« (*quiet room*) schreibt. Davon verspricht er sich die Aufschlüsse, die ihm der Patient sonst vorenthalten würde.

In diesen flüchtig an die Wand geworfenen, subjektiv gefärbten Schilderungen entsteht nun facettenartig Burts seitheriger Erlebnishorizont und sein Persönlichkeitspuzzle. Der Patient beschreibt assoziativ die aus seiner Sicht markanten Vorfälle in Familie und Schule, wobei Wichtiges und weniger Wichtiges in kindlicher Manier gleichrangig nebeneinander gestellt wird: »I can hear the clock in the living room. It says tick tock. My mum always has a cup of coffee. She stares at the wall. She zups it« (S. 43).[9] Seine Schilderungen erwecken den Eindruck, dass er zu den meisten Erwachsenen seines Umfelds ein gespanntes bis gebrochenes Verhältnis hat. In seinem Empfinden der *phoniness*, der Unehrlichkeit und Hinterlist der Erwachsenen, ist Burt Salingers Romanfigur Holden Caulfield nicht unähnlich: »[Dr Nevele] smiled at me but it was phony baloney« (S. 33).[10] Die elterliche Erziehung erscheint überstreng und von nicht nachvollziehbaren, ja angsterzeugenden Verboten geprägt, die sich tief in das Gedächtnis des Jungen eingegraben haben: »[...] never cross Seven Mile Road without a grown-up or I will get run over« (S. 172). Burt fühlt sich ungeliebt und den Eltern lästig: »[...] because I

9 Vgl. dazu Cynthia Joyce; »*When I Was Five I Killed Myself*«, in: *New York Times*, 30. Juli 2000: »[Buten] captures the free associative randomness of childlike thinking, in which thoughts large and small hold equal weight.«

10 Vgl. J. D. Salinger, *The Catcher in the Rye*, Harmondsworth: Penguin, 1958: »One of the biggest reasons I left Elkton Hills was because I was surrounded by phonies« (S. 17 f.); »It was partly a phoney kind of friendly, but at least he always said hello« (S. 29); »[...] old Ernie turned around on his stool and gave this very phoney, humble bow« (S. 89) u. a.

think I'm adopted« (S. 155); »Once my dad said why don't I put myself in an envelope and mail myself to Alaska but I said I didn't have enough stamps« (S. 165). Seine erwachende vorpubertäre Sexualität wird von ihm als »komisches Gefühl« wahrgenommen, weil das Thema von den Eltern nicht angesprochen, gar tabuisiert worden ist: »The pen gave me a funny feeling in my stomach, under my stomach« (S. 46); »Sometimes the train turned a corner and Miss Iris slid against me and it made me feel funny« (S. 74); »[Jessica] showed it [the brassiere] to me, it made me feel funny. It was wrong. I'm not supposed to look at them« (S. 186); vgl. auch S. 87. Die Eltern-Sohn-Beziehung wird durch Burts Antwortbrief an Jessica im Schlusskapitel schlaglichtartig erhellt. Seine unbeantwortete, leise Frage »Is anybody there?« auf dem Flur vor dem dunklen Elternschlafzimmer nach einem Albtraum lässt zwei Deutungsmöglichkeiten zu. Entweder sind die Eltern ausgegangen, ohne einen Babysitter zu bestellen, oder aber sie sind da, doch der Sohn wagt sie aus Angst vor Strafe nicht zu wecken. Die Briefzeilen sind jedenfalls eindringlicher Beweis für Burts Gefühl, emotional im Stich gelassen zu sein.

Objekte wie seine geliebte Wolldecke »blankee« (»At home is blankee. He is blue. I have had him since I was a baby. My mom wants to throw him away but I won't let her«, S. 36), Stofftiere wie Monkey Cuddles (S. 165) oder sein Panda (S. 169) figurieren für Burt als personifizierter Liebesersatz. Die selbstgebastelte Marionette Jerry the Puppet scheint ihm den Freund zu ersetzen: »Then I kissed him. ›Good night, Jerry the Puppet [...] I'm glad I made you« (S. 141 f.).

Mit Gleichaltrigen verbindet Burt ebenfalls recht wenig. Außer einer Sandkastenfreundschaft mit Shrubs hegt er nur für Jessica, eine gleichaltrige Mitschülerin aus der Parallelklasse, tiefere Gefühle. Er liebt ihre Augen (»her eyes had diamonds in them«), ihre Direktheit, Unerschrockenheit und Unangepasstheit. Jessica lehnt sich gegen Autorität auf, die sich lediglich auf Status oder Alter beruft (Kap. 3, 9). Sie hat einen unbändigen Freiheitsdrang (S. 81). In ihrer rätselhaften Unberechenbarkeit und ihren unvorhersehbaren Reaktionen bleibt sie für den Jungen sonderbar anziehend: »I couldn't tell with Jessica« (S. 172). Wie Burt ist sie voll überbordender Fantasie (S. 160f.), wie er erliegt sie immer wieder ihrem Hang zu ausgefallenen Notlügen (S. 174). Bei beiden sind die Grenzen und Übergänge zwischen Fantastik, Tagträumen, Lügen und Realität fließend.

Auch unter der Lehrerschaft findet Burt nicht die Bezugsperson, der er sich in Ermangelung elterlicher Zuwendung und Zuneigung anvertrauen könnte. Mit Ausnahme von Miss Iris (Kap. 9) kommen Burts Lehrer eher schlecht weg. Sie sind als Erzieher überfordert und weitgehend verständnislos. Außer Androhung und Vollzug drastischer Strafen fällt ihnen wenig ein, sadistische Gemeinheit (Miss Krepnik), kalter Sarkasmus (Mr. Stomatsky) oder Brutalität (Miss Filmer) sind an der Tagesordnung. Unter den Lehrern sind die jeweiligen Erziehungsmaßnahmen umstritten, und es regiert der blanke Hass: »The two teachers got real angry and looked daggers at each other« (S. 94).

Das Unverständnis zwischen Kindern und Erwachsenen, die fehlende Antenne füreinander und die daraus resultierende kindliche Vereinsamung, die Fehlentwicklungen und Beinahe-Katastrophen, sind somit zentrales Thema des Romans. In vielen Episoden zeigen sich die unterschiedlichen Wahrnehmungsebenen in aller Deutlichkeit. Für Burts eher oberflächliche Mutter ist Dr. Nevele »a terrific guy« (S. 69),[11] den Sohn dagegen Hassfigur. In Kapitel 8 steht Burt beim Zahnarzt Todesängste aus, für seine Mutter ist der vorgenommene Eingriff eine Bagatelle: »Now see, wasn't so bad, was it?« (S. 63). Der Bombenalarm ist für die Lehrerin eine Routineübung, für die Kinder Jessica und Burt, die die Bedrohung durch den Kalten Krieg der fünfziger und frühen sechziger Jahre gedanklich und gefühlsmäßig nicht verarbeitet haben, ist er existenzielle Bedrohung (»It [the News] has Russians who will bury us«, S. 7; »My dad is going to build a shelter in

---

11 Ihre Oberflächlichkeit und ihr Mangel an Differenzierungsvermögen zeigen sich zum Beispiel in der Überstrapazierung der Vokabel »terrific« (S. 69f.), die sie fünfmal verwendet.

our cellar. He saw it in a magazine«, S. 21). Für Burts Vater ist der Tod des Mädchens in den Nachrichten etwas Alltägliches (»It's just the rules«, S. 8), für Burt dagegen Anlass, sich (fast) umzubringen. Für Jessica ist der Tod des Vaters ein traumatisches Erlebnis (Kap. 18), ihrer Mutter ist es wichtig, dass die Polster im Wohnzimmer durch die Trauergemeinde keinen Schaden nehmen (S. 183). Auf der anderen Seite kann Burt bei einem Ausflug in den Zoo seinen ausgestopften Alligator nicht von den bissigen echten Exemplaren unterscheiden. Er riskiert am Reptilgehege Kopf und Kragen, was die Lehrerin Miss Iris fast zum Wahnsinn treibt (Kap. 9).

Doch bei all den überwiegend desolaten menschlichen Beziehungen gibt es einen Lichtblick, der das düstere Bild etwas aufhellt. Während zwischen Dr. Nevele und Burt Sprachlosigkeit und ein Vertrauensvakuum herrschen, schafft es der junge Psychologe Rudyard Walton auf andere Art, eine Beziehung zum Patienten Burt aufzubauen. Er begibt sich absichtsvoll auf dessen Ebene, versucht, sich empathisch in seine Gefühlswelt hineinzuversetzen. Durch geschicktes Vorgehen schafft es Walton schließlich, Burt zu einem Erfolgserlebnis beim Schwimmen zu verhelfen (S. 113). Er erwirbt dessen Vertrauen in erster Linie dadurch, dass er sich nicht wie ein »Halbgott in Weiß« geriert: »He was a doctor but he didn't act like a doctor. He acted like a little boy. Like me« (S. 57). Auch im Fall des stark verhaltensgestörten Carl schafft er durch Imitation von dessen Symptomen die für einen Therapieerfolg unabdingbare Akzeptanz. Fast zwangsläufig wird aus dem »redhaired man« für Burt schließlich »Rudyard« (S. 68) und mithin so etwas wie ein väterlicher Freund. Es liegt sicher nahe, hier eine autobiografische Reminiszenz Butens zu vermuten.[12]

---

12 Vgl. Guttman, 1987, S. 1: »[Buten's] PhD thesis dealt with empathy toward the patient: ›My work is based on imitation, that is, being autistic with an autistic child. This creates a relationship between us that would not happen otherwise […]‹. The goal is not necessarily a modification in behavior, but an exploration of possibility, an understanding through assimilating the patient's symptoms. Buten has often paid a high price for his controversial techniques […].«

Ironischerweise wird Walton wegen seiner unkonventionel-
len Methode und seines abweichenden Therapieansatzes, der
den Behandlungsnormen der von Nevele vertretenen »klassi-
schen« Psychiatrie zuwiderläuft, abgestraft und muss auf Neveles Geheiß den Fall Rembrandt abgeben. Dieser hat mittler-
weile ganz auf Härte gegenüber Burt umgeschaltet. Er isoliert
ihn völlig von der Außenwelt, indem er keinerlei Besuche zu-
lässt: »And now there isn't anybody. I wish I was home. I wish
I wasn't anywhere« (S. 194). Nevele erlaubt nur den Brief-
wechsel zwischen Burt, seinen Eltern und seinem Bruder Jeffrey. Er unterschlägt zudem Jessicas Briefe. Zwar sitzt Nevele
am längeren Hebel, doch wird ihm von Walton in einer Art
ironisierendem »Gegengutachten« unmissverständlich klar gemacht, dass Burt in dieser Anstalt fehl am Platz ist, dass er
weder verrückt noch verhaltensgestört oder gar kriminell,
sondern Opfer einer verklemmten Sexualmoral der Erwachsenen ist (S. 114 ff.). Seine Schuld ist lediglich eine Projektion
dieser Doppelmoral der Erwachsenen auf ihn: »We have met
the enemy, and it is us« (S. 116).

In der Tat gehen die sexuelle Annäherung und der vermut-
liche Koitus (S. 187 ff.) von beiden Kindern aus. Jessica und
Burt hassen ihren Kinderstatus und sind es leid, von den Erwachsenen gemaßregelt, aber nicht ernst genommen zu werden (S. 180 bzw. 187). Beide suchen miteinander die körperli-
che und seelische Nähe und Wärme, die ihnen von den Erwachsenen vorenthalten werden.

Mit dem Einverständnis und der tätigen Mithilfe Jessicas
(»She rolled over and leaned on me with her side on me«,
S. 188), beschließt Burt, ihr beidseitiges »Kindsein« zu be-
enden: »I'll make it so we won't be children any more«
(ebd.). Was in großer gegenseitiger Zärtlichkeit und Unschuld
zwischen den beiden nach Zuneigung Hungernden abläuft,
wird jäh von Jessicas Mutter unterbrochen, die wie ein Ra-
cheengel und in der Manier einer Furie über Burt herfällt. Er
wird von ihr einseitig kriminalisiert, die Einweisung in ein
Heim wird ihm von ihr wie ein Menetekel verkündet: »I'm
going to take care of you though, don't worry. You'll never do

this again, not to my little girl, or anyone. Do you hear me?« (S. 190).

Trotz des insgesamt wehmütigen und melancholischen Grundtons der Erzählung gibt es immer wieder heitere Episoden, die mit Burts naiv-entwaffnender Sicht der Dinge zusammenhängen (z.B. die Weckszene am Anfang von Kap. 8). Wie in seiner Arbeit als Clown ist es auch als Autor für Buten unumstößliches Prinzip, dass Ernstes und Heiteres eine geglückte Verbindung eingehen müssen, damit sich Betroffenheit und Rührung beim Hörer-Leser einstellen.[13]

Buten versteht es geschickt, die Kindersprache einzufangen, wobei ihm sicherlich seine jahrelange Arbeit mit Kindern und Jugendlichen half. So ist der Roman kindgemäß weitgehend in parataktischem »Sprechstil« gehalten, mit additiven Reihungen, assoziativem *Clustering*, und oftmals ohne Verwendung von Konjunktionen: »He looked at me, he was very large« (S. 23); »It was the red-haired man, he came back« (S. 36); »Jessica's house was the one with blue shutters. Bricks and wood. Not red bricks, though, mauve« (S. 25).

Kindliche Paraphrasierungen mangels des treffenden Wortes sind ein von Buten häufig eingesetztes Stilelement mit witzigem Nebeneffekt: »She had on a red dress with like waves in it« (S. 34); »new desks, they have hard stuff on the top like a kitchen« (gemeint ist eine Art Resopalplatte) (S. 156); »just a thing on the bottom that went back and forth back and forth« (gemeint ist das Uhrenpendel) (S. 182). Umständliche Formulierungen, die dadurch fast originell werden, bringen den Leser häufig zum Schmunzeln: »It makes you upside down« (»es dreht einem den Magen um«) (S. 62); »I couldn't not look« (»ich musste ganz einfach hinsehen«) (S. 161).

Diese kindlichen Umständlichkeiten führen teils zu witzigen Vergleichen (»the penguins who wore tuxedos«, S. 75), teils zu skurrilen sprachlichen Fehlleistungen: »She went in is

13 Vgl. das Interview mit Stanley Péan: »Tout le monde devrait savoir que si tu veux émouvoir quelqu'un, lui présenter uniquement de la la tristesse ne marche jamais [...]«. www.librairiepantoute.qc.ca/magazine/articles/buten. asp

how I knew« (I knew because she went in there) (S. 25); »Also
we have a back door, not side« (ebd.).

Die Sprechsyntax Burts steht in starkem Kontrast zum Wis-
senschaftskauderwelsch der Gutachten von Dr. Nevele, dem
der junge Patient verständnislos gegenübersteht: »»Maybe
Burton can express himself better in writing than he can verbally.‹ I don't know what verbally is. I think it is some kind of
vegetables« (S. 32). Über sein eigenes Gutachten, das ihm Nevele unverständlicherweise überlässt, sagt Burt Folgendes:
»[...] I don't understand it. It is too big words« (S. 41). Buten
selbst scheint dem hochgestochenen Wissenschaftsjargon seiner Berufsgenossen, der lediglich Pseudotiefgang vortäuscht,
höchst kritisch gegenüberzustehen.[14]

Dass eine Geschichte wie die von Buten erzählte im amerikanischen Kontext einer oftmals bigotten und wirklichkeits-
fernen Doppelmoral durchaus realistisch erscheint, bewies der
im Jahre 1999 von den Medien in aller Welt ausgeschlachtete
Fall eines elfjährigen Schweizer Jungen, der den Mühlen der
amerikanischen Justiz mit knapper Not entkam.[15] Auch da-
mals schienen einer aufgeklärten Weltöffentlichkeit Anlass
und die von der US-Justiz ergriffenen Maßnahmen unverhält-
nismäßig auseinander zu klaffen.

When I Was Five I Killed Myself ist ein in vieler Hinsicht
beachtliches Werk. Auch wenn der Antagonismus zwischen
dem jungen, einfühlsamen Psychologen Walton und dem fest-
gefahrenen, sturen, bisweilen dämonisierten Dr. Nevele auf
manche Leser etwas klischeehaft und holzschnittartig wirken

14 Vgl. ebd. »Jamais je ne psychanalyse mes personnages. Je fais de la littéra-
ture pour me libérer de tout ça, parce que les psy [psychiatres] sont telle-
ment bêtes parfois, avec leur jargon à la con«.
15 »On 10 Nov. [1999] Colorado judge dismisses charges against an eleven-
year-old Swiss boy who was accused of aggravated incest and sexual as-
sault on a child (his five-year-old half-sister). After a neighbor told the
authorities that the boy had been seen touching his sister in the yard of
the parents' house, he was arrested at night, taken away in handcuffs and
detained for six weeks.« http://www.univnancy2.fr/CEAA/CRESAB/chro-
no-us02_00-mp.html

mag, so überwiegen die überzeugend geschriebenen Passagen und die eindrucksvollen Aspekte des Romans bei weitem. Das Buch besticht durch Vielschichtigkeit, Sprachkraft, feine Beobachtungsgabe auf Seiten des Autors für die komplizierte Seelenlage von Problemjugendlichen, hohe Sensibilität und Originalität der Darstellung. Buten ist zu wünschen, dass ihm, dem »Anonymus« in seinem Geburtsland,[16] mit der Neuauflage endlich auch dort der Erfolg beschieden ist, der ihm eigentlich zusteht.

Ernst Kemmner

16 Vgl. Johnson, 1994, S. 1.

Inhalt

Englische Fremdsprachentexte

IN RECLAMS UNIVERSAL-BIBLIOTHEK

Dramen

Edward Albee: Who's Afraid of Virginia Woolf? 206 S. UB 9073

Samuel Beckett: Waiting for Godot. 147 S. UB 9214

Five English Short Plays. Brenton, Bond, Stoppard, Pinter, Churchill. 210 S. UB 9062

Arthur Miller: The Crucible. 224 S. UB 9257 – Death of a Salesman. 171 S. UB 9172

Eugene O'Neill: Long Day's Journey into Night. 216 S. UB 9252

J. B. Priestley: An Inspector Calls. 117 S. UB 9218

Willy Russell: Educating Rita. 132 S. UB 9040 – Shirley Valentine. 79 S. UB 9071

Peter Shaffer: Amadeus. 199 S. UB 9219

William Shakespeare: Hamlet. 261 S. UB 9292 – Macbeth. 167 S. UB 9220 – The Merchant of Venice 184 S. UB 9050 – A Midsummer Night's Dream. 160 S. UB 9247 – Romeo and Juliet. 219 S. UB 9005

Bernard Shaw: Mrs Warren's Profession. 198 S. UB 9166 – Pygmalion. 197 S. UB 9266

Tom Stoppard: Rosencrantz and Guildenstern are Dead. 171 S. UB 9185

John Millington Synge: The Playboy of the Western World. 128 S. UB 9211

Oscar Wilde: The Importance of Being Earnest. 141 S. UB 9267 – Lady Windermere's Fan. 101 S. UB 9187

Thornton Wilder: Our Town. 127 S. UB 9168

Tennessee Williams: Cat on a Hot Tin Roof. 224 S. UB 9039 – The Glass Menagerie. 149 S. UB 9178 – A Streetcar Named Desire. 199 S. UB 9240

Philipp Reclam jun. Stuttgart